SO-BVN-683

Electricity: How It Works

Percy Dunsheath

ELECTRICITY:
HOW IT WORKS

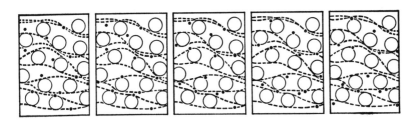

ILLUSTRATED BY JOHN TEPPICH

Thomas Y. Crowell Company
NEW YORK

Contents

U. S.1122165

CHAPTER 1

Static Electricity

Most of us are curious to see how things work, so let us start the story of electricity with an experiment.

Take an empty metal candy box about an inch and a half deep, a sheet of window glass about the same size or larger, and a silk scarf. Cut out from a sheet of tissue paper a few figures of men with top hats and dogs with curly tails each about half the height of the box. Dry everything thoroughly in a warm oven, then put the figures in the box and cover them with the glass. Rub the glass hard with the warm silk and presently you will see the men and dogs become agitated. The harder you rub, the more excited they get, jumping up to the glass and quivering backward and forward in a lively manner.

If you live where the air is dry, you will have no difficulty with this experiment; but, if the air is humid, the glass and the silk must both be very warm for success. The great English physicist Professor Tyndall was fond of this and similar experiments, but he evidently had difficulty in carrying them out due to the damp climate of London for he wrote many years ago:

"Skill in the art of experimenting does not come of itself, it is only to be acquired by labour. By practice alone you learn to dance and to play. This also is the only way of learning the art of experiment. You must not therefore be daunted by your clumsi-

A simple electrical experiment. Static electricity generated by silk on glass attracts paper figures.

ness at first, you must overcome it, and acquire skill in the art by *repetition.*"

If you have been persistent, you have demonstrated the most fundamental aspect of electricity; you have made electricity by *friction*—static electricity we call it. But this is not quite true. Electricity is everywhere. It was in the paper before you started the experiment, so you could not possibly have made it. You simply showed that it existed.

What you really did was to separate two kinds of electricity—*positive* electricity and *negative* electricity. When they are separated, they produce all kinds of effects which compel our attention. Examples of static electricity due to friction are well known and often occur unintentionally. In dry climates you only need to shuffle across the carpet to get a shock on touching the door knob. The friction of your shoes on the carpet has charged your body, and this charge is discharged to the door knob with a resulting tingling sensation in your finger. Pull a nylon garment quickly over your head in the dark and you will see and hear tiny crackling sparks as the charges which you have produced by friction discharge themselves. Hang up your nylon stockings, pajamas, or nightgown and stroke them; they follow your hand as you draw it away.

The existence of static electricity has been known for many centuries. The earliest observation of all must have been that of lightning, the most powerful of natural electrical phenomena. We shall consider later how static charges produce lightning, but for the moment we shall keep to practical experiments more within our grasp.

For thousands of years people have been interested in a substance called *amber,* a semiprecious mineral which is a fossilized resin. Originally the resin drained from a species of pine tree now extinct and then hardened for centuries in the soil, forming amber. It is found principally along the Baltic coast of Europe, and has been the object of an active trade.

When a piece of amber is rubbed with fur, it will pick up light objects such as dry leaves. The person usually associated with the discovery of this phenomenon is Thales of Miletus who lived in Asia Minor about six centuries before Christ. We don't know much about Thales, but it appears from what we are told by such authorities as Aristotle and Plutarch that he was a keen businessman as well as an engineer and mathematician. He was also wise enough to appreciate the advantages of travel to study other countries, and he crossed the Mediterranean to visit Egypt. After seeing the way the Egyptians laid out their fields, he originated the science of geometry with important results. He also learned how to predict eclipses of the sun. When you have learned all there is to know about electricity, you could do worse than go back and study Thales and his successors in the field of geometry. It is a fascinating story.

It is of interest to note here that the Greek word for the substance amber was ἤλεκτρον, translated *electron.* The sixteenth-century English physician Dr. William Gilbert adopted the word *electric* in describing the various effects of static electricity.

There is one more electrical discovery we must give the early scientists credit for. They knew that a person could receive a violent electric shock by coming into contact with a fish called the torpedo. We even read that rheumatoid Roman emperors sometimes had one of these unpleasant companions put in the bath with them hoping the shock would cure their rheumatism.

In recent years serious research work has been carried out on the nature of the electric discharge given out by one of the various kinds of electric fish—the electric eel (*Electrophorus electricus*) often found in the tropical waters of South America. This creature causes much trouble in shallow water where horses or cattle walk or drink, and it can indeed give fatal shocks. The experiments show that an eel can give as much as 600 volts when fully grown, and even baby eels only one inch long can give a reasonably tickling shock. The amusing thing about an electric eel is that the head end is always positive and the tail end negative and they can detect one another electrically; for, in addition to emitting a discharge intermittently, they are capable of detecting a discharge from an external source during their own quiescent intervals. A piece of metal charged positively will attract an electric eel even in the dark; he thinks it is the head of a friend, and rushes madly to meet him, only to be sadly disappointed on finding a piece of metal.

How does static electricity work?

Let us take a rod of *ebonite* (hard rubber)—a fountain pen will do—and rub it with a piece of warm dry flannel. Or as an alternative take a glass rod and rub it with a piece of silk. In both cases the result will *appear* to be the same. The rod will be found to attract light objects such as strips of tissue paper or small pieces of thin metal foil.

There are many other combinations of material in the form of rod and wiper that act in the same way, but electricity is an exact science so we must now go a stage further in our investigation.

Our knowledge must be exact. Make a very light ball about half an inch in diameter and suspend it on a silk thread. Balsa wood, used for making model aircraft, or anything very light, will serve the purpose. After carefully rounding it with a sharp knife, paint the ball with aluminum paint. It is worth while to make half a dozen of these balls.

Having suspended the ball by means of an insulating thread of silk to prevent any charge from leaking away, rub the ebonite rod and touch the ball with it. Rub the rod again and this time bring it near but not touching the charged ball. You will at once make an interesting observation—the ball moves *away* from the rod which charged it.

Now repeat the experiment, first charging the ball as before with the rubbed ebonite rod, but the second time bringing up a glass rod which has been rubbed with silk. The ball is attracted and not repelled!

Thus we see that there are two kinds of electricity, the kind which appears on a rubbed glass rod and that which appears on a rubbed ebonite rod. In describing his famous experiments

An ebonite or glass rod rubbed with flannel or silk becomes electrified and repels a suspended ball which it has touched. A rubbed glass rod attracts a suspended ball which has been previously charged by touching a rubbed ebonite rod.

carried out in Philadelphia about 1747 Benjamin Franklin named the kind of electricity on glass *positive* electricity. The electricity on ebonite he called *negative*.

We have seen how curious things happen to small bodies when they become electrified; the rubbed glass plate makes paper men and dogs stand and move, and the rubbed glass and ebonite rods attract light objects to them. We must know more about this effect of a charged body on an uncharged one. This is sometimes difficult to understand. But the explanation is simple and quite illuminating. When a charged body is brought close to an insulated uncharged one but without actually making contact, it induces a charge on the near portions of an opposite kind and a charge on the remote portions of a similar kind. Thus a positively charged body induces a negative charge on the near end of the uncharged body and a positive charge on the far end. It is as though an uncharged body normally has an equal amount of negative and positive charge canceling each other and that, when a charged body is brought near, these two kinds become separated from one another. Removal of the external inducing charge restores the condition of balance and the insulated body remains uncharged.

If, while the state of unbalance due to the proximity of the charging body continues, the latter is allowed to touch, then the induced near-end charge is canceled by the contact. The far-end charge remains and, when the inducing charge is taken away, the body is charged the same as the far end. A further simple experiment will throw light on the subject. Set up two suspended balsa balls on silk threads about a foot and a half long. Suspend them two to three inches apart. We will charge the balls in three different ways. First we charge one by touching it with the rubbed glass rod and the other with the rubbed ebonite rod, so giving the balls opposite charges—one of them positive and the other negative. What happens?

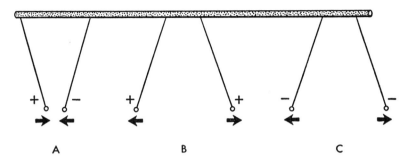

Unlike charges attract; like charges repel. (A) Balls both charged, one with glass rod and one with ebonite rod, attract each other. (B) Both balls charged with glass rod repel one another. (C) Both balls charged with ebonite rod repel one another.

The balls are drawn to one another.

In the next place we charge them both with the glass rod, and they repel one another. Finally we charge both with the ebonite rod, and again they repel one another.

We have in this simple experiment discovered for ourselves a most important fundamental law in electrostatics. This may be stated as follows:

A positive charge attracts a negative charge.

A negative charge attracts a positive charge.

A positive charge repels a positive charge.

A negative charge repels a negative charge.

Unlike charges attract one another.

Like charges repel one another.

A positively charged glass rod placed near a piece of paper draws, or induces, a negative charge in the near end of the paper and sends the equal positive charge in the paper scuttling off as fast and as far as it can go.

That is why the paper is attracted. The induced opposite charge does the trick!

There is a peculiarity about the ultimate behavior of an object attracted to a charged rod. On touching the rod the object does not remain stuck to it; after a short interval of time it shoots off again. Here is the reason. As the object carrying a small induced charge of an opposite sign to that of the rod approaches the rod, it is attracted to it. When it touches the rod, however, this small charge is overcome by the larger charge on the rod and the object then has the same kind of charge as that on the rod and is repelled.

Suppose the glass rod has a positive charge represented by the figure 10 and the object a negative charge represented by the figure 1. Then when they come into contact the negative 1 cancels one of the positive 10. The rod thus has only 9 and the object no charge at all. But at once the rod gives up some of the remaining 9, leaving both the rod and the object positively charged. Therefore repulsion follows and the object flies away again. This is not the full explanation but is sufficient to indicate what takes place.

A simple instrument for indicating electric charges depends for its action on the repulsion between two similar charges. It is known as the gold-leaf electroscope and was invented nearly two hundred years ago. In this instrument two strips of gold leaf hang from a metal rod inside a glass container which has metal strips attached to the outside. When the rod is charged, the leaves in contact with it are both similarly charged and repel one another. The extent of the deflection is an indication of the magnitude of the charge.

Another very practical and useful piece of electrical equipment which you will come across many times in all branches of electrical work is the *condenser*. We have seen how a charge on one body induces an opposite charge on a second nearby body and holds it by attraction. The effect is very much increased by bringing the objects closer together and increasing their size—that is, by enlarging the areas of the objects facing one another. When we deliberately arrange two conductors, such as two metal plates, near one another and prevent them from coming in contact with

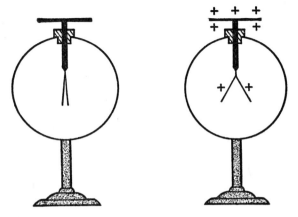

The gold-leaf electroscope.

one another by separating them with a thickness of glass or waxed paper, we produce an electrical condenser or, as it is sometimes called, a *capacitor*.

The simplest form of condenser consists of two flat metal plates held a short distance apart, one above the other, in the air. Such a condenser can be charged by touching the upper plate with a charged rod while the lower plate is grounded (that is, connected to the ground and all surrounding objects). By the application of the rod several times, the charges can be built up or stored in the condenser. (See illustration on page 10.)

The earliest electric condenser was the famous Leyden jar which was discovered accidentally about the end of 1745 by Cunaeus at Leyden, in Holland. Cunaeus, a student, was helping Professor Musschenbroek to conduct electricity, which was then thought to be a sort of fluid, into a bottle of water through a nail in the cork. Cunaeus was holding the jar in his hand and all went well until he touched the nail with the other hand and received a violent shock. Since that date the principle of storing electricity by means of a condenser has been developed in many directions, particularly in radio.

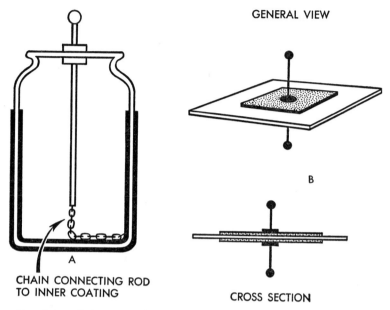

GENERAL VIEW

B

CHAIN CONNECTING ROD
TO INNER COATING

CROSS SECTION

Two forms of electric condenser. (A) Leyden jar. Metallic coatings inside and outside a glass jar. (B) Flat-plate condenser. Metallic coatings on two sides of a sheet of glass or other insulating material. In practical condensers the flat sheets are rolled up and embodied in a wax-filled container.

All substances may be classified as conductors or insulators. Conductors, like the metals, conduct electricity freely. Copper is the one most generally used, with aluminum a close second, for underground cables, overhead transmission lines, and domestic wiring. Substances like rubber, porcelain, and the plastic materials offer a high resistance to the passage of electricity and are known as insulators. In between the two extreme classes are substances like wood, undried paper, and certain chemical products. When a material is employed in electrical equipment for its particularly good insulating properties it is known as a *dielectric*.

The dielectric of a condenser is simply that component which separates two opposing metallic plates with positive and negative charges. In the simplest condenser, consisting of two metal plates, the dielectric is air. In the Leyden jar the dielectric is glass, the substance of the bottle which keeps the outside metal coating separated electrically from the inside coating—in the early form separated from the water contents which communicated with the rod and knob. In both forms the glass is the dielectric. Other dielectric materials used in practical condensers are oil, varnish, wax, etc., or paper impregnated with one of these substances. Mica in the form of sheets or tubes of porcelain is also used. During recent years new synthetic materials such as polyethylene, polyvinylchloride (P.V.C.), and silicone have been developed as dielectrics. All these substances increase the capacity of a condenser over that which it would have with air as the dielectric, and the relative increase is known as the dielectric constant of the substance. A glass condenser can hold about six times as much as an air condenser; therefore, it is said to have a dielectric constant of 6.

There is much in the study of electricity that must depend on the effects which it produces. We cannot see it as we see other physical things around us, such as trees, skyscrapers, and buses.

There is, however, a very useful convention for getting a clearer idea and that is the line of force.

In the early part of the last century that remarkable Englishman Michael Faraday developed the idea of a field of force composed of lines of force connecting charged objects. It is as though a positive charge sent out these imaginary lines and each line finished somewhere on a negative charge. In a condenser these lines cross the dielectric from the positive plate to the negative. When two balsa balls are charged oppositely—one negative and one positive—the lines of force pass across the intervening space from one to the other. If, however, both charges are positive, the lines from one avoid the other; similarly, when both are negative. In these two cases of similar charge the lines of force from one

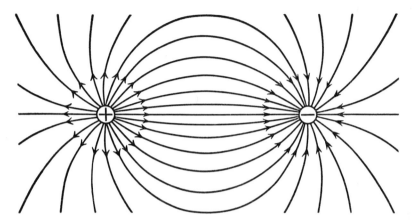

Lines of electrostatic force. Invisible lines of force emerge from a positively charged object and enter a negatively charged one.

sphere—which cannot land on the other—find a finishing point on the walls of the room and other surrounding objects.

Faraday supposed that these lines of force were in tension, like elastic threads, and that they repelled one another sideways so that the unlike charges are drawn together and the like charges repelled, as shown in the diagram.

So far we have spoken entirely of electricity generated by the

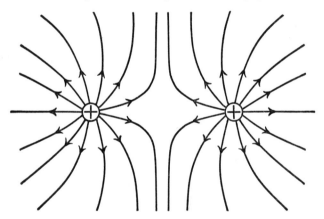

Lines of force from a particular charge, + or —, avoid a similar charge.

rubbed rod (and of course the sheet of glass). But you will understand that such devices are not very practical for producing large quantities of electricity, and from the early days many mechanical devices have been invented for the purpose. In the friction machines, cylinders of glass were rotated against rubbing pads and the charge was picked up on pointed collectors. Induction machines followed, the most famous being the Wimshurst influence machine (still used in many American schools for electrostatic demonstrations).

The induction machine for generating static electricity depends on the principle first evolved by Volta at the end of the eighteenth century when he invented what he called the *electrophorus*. In the construction of this device Volta poured a composition of resin into a flat dish and let it solidify. He then generated a charge on the solid resin by rubbing, and he placed a metal plate provided with an insulating handle on the resin.

At this stage the negative charge on the resin surface induced a positive charge on the lower surface of the plate and repelled

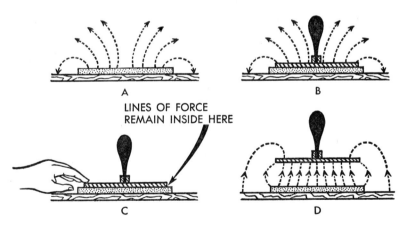

The electrophorus. (A) Resin slab charged by rubbing. (B) Upper plate applied. (C) Upper plate discharged. (D) Upper plate raised and exhibiting induced charge.

an equal negative charge to the upper side of the plate. He then touched the upper surface of the plate which released this negative charge and then lifted the plate off by the insulated handle, which carried away with it the remaining induced positive charge. With this he charged a Leyden jar. By repeating the process Volta was able to build up a charge many times the magnitude of that originally on the slab.

The electrophorus is very interesting and really very simple, although many people do not seem to understand the action. The electrophorus is not a device for generating a charge of electricity by rubbing a slab of resin and then picking it off with a plate having an insulating handle. It is, actually, a machine for producing a charge, that is, for separating the two kinds of electricity on an object. The initial charge on the resin slab is required only to start the action and, apart from slight leakage, the charge remains indefinitely on the slab. The upper movable plate is the object in which electricity is separated into its two components, positive and negative. It has no charge; but, as it is lowered over the charged slab by the handle, the negative charge on the slab attracts the positive electricity in the upper plate and repels the negative electricity; the lower surface of the plate thus becomes charged positively and the upper surface, negatively.

While the movable plate is in close proximity to the charged slab of resin, its upper surface is touched, and the negative electricity escapes to ground via the operator's body. The positive electricity on the lower surface, however, still remains bound there by the attraction of the resin. It is trapped for the time being; but, when we lift the plate by the handle, the attraction of the resin disappears and we have caught the positive charge. This positive charge tries to find the negative charge with which it was formerly associated, but it has gone. It has already been led carefully away to the ground, and the positive charge has the whole plate to itself. We can use it to charge a condenser or for any other purpose.

You may say, "But surely, when you stand the metal plate on the resin slab, it conducts the negative charge directly from the slab and becomes negatively charged, not positively as you have stated." That is a correct observation, but it is not the whole story.

The slab of resin is not dead flat, and the plate actually rests on only a few peaks. These peaks are certainly discharged, but over the greater part of the resin area there is a slight air gap between it and the metal plate, and this is the explanation. The positive charge induced in the plate over the air gap far outweighs the small negative leakage at the peaks; and, as the resin is a good insulator, the negative charge in the air gap does not leak up to the peaks.

An understanding of the electrophorus will help make clear the action of the Wimshurst influence machine. Two disks of glass, say *A* and *B,* can be rotated in opposite directions by means of a handle, pulleys, and belts. Each disk has tin-foil sectors stuck to it, and on their way around they can make contact with wire brushes. A small positive charge is given to a sector on disk *A* by a rubbed glass rod and the machine is started. This sector on *A* with its positive charge comes opposite an uncharged sector on disk *B* moving in the opposite direction, and at the same moment the latter comes in contact with a fixed discharging brush. The *A* charge induces a negative charge on the *B* sector and repels the other half of *B*'s electricity, the positive half, which escapes through the brush. The *B* sector now moves out of contact with the discharging brush and away from the influence of the charge on the *A* sector and carries with it the trapped negative charge, the action being exactly like that of the electrophorus. This negative charge then moves on and comes opposite an uncharged sector on disk *A,* which again has a discharging brush on the outside. Here the negative charge on the *B* sector develops a positive charge on the *A* sector, and so it goes on. The positive charges on the *A* sectors build up as do the negative charges on the *B* sectors. Collecting points situated farther around the disk ultimately bring out both charges to the terminals ready for use.

You will see from what I have said about the electrophorus and the Wimshurst influence machine that the electric charge moves about on a conducting object, depending on both external and internal influences. If the object is hollow, the charge always goes to the outside surface, as we can confirm by charging a hollow sphere and testing the inside surface through a small hole. Even if we introduce a charge onto the inner surface, it flies at once to the outside and, like the Leyden jar, provides a simple means of collecting a charge and holding it.

Sometimes we want to prevent an object or an instrument from receiving a charge itself. We can achieve this by enclosing the item in a surrounding box of wire mesh. This is known as a Faraday cage and is sometimes used to protect an operator working on a highly charged instrument. If the person is entirely inside the cage, no harm can come to him, though the cage may be charged to such an extent that the outside surface is emitting sparks into the air.

There is another interesting phenomenon in connection with the distribution of charge over the surface of an electrical body. This phenomenon is due to the shape of the body. On a sphere isolated in space the charge spreads uniformly over the surface, but if the body is pear-shaped, the charge crowds into the shallow part—the stalk end of the pear. If we go further and convert the stalk end into a sharp point, the charge so crowds itself onto this point that it produces some remarkable effects: the point produces a wind due to the charge's forcing its way off at the point and thus charging air molecules and blowing them away by repulsion. An interesting toy can be made by fixing four pieces of pointed wire about one inch long, with the ends bent over at a right angle, to a spindle lying across two insulated horizontal rails and then charging the arrangement. The pointed ends produce the electric wind and the reaction rotates the "mill," which thus travels along the rails.

When examined in the dark a pointed object, heavily charged, gives off a purple glow and a sizzling sound. In thundery weather and during dry frosty snowstorms such discharges take place on the masts of ships and have been known by sailors for many centuries as St. Elmo's fire, so named after their patron saint.

Today electrostatic charges are being produced on a large scale for various purposes by power-driven machines known as Van de Graaff generators and some are capable of generating many millions of volts. Because it is possible to make a Van de Graaff generator on a small scale to give quite strong discharges, it is worth spending a little time describing the principle of operation of the large Van de Graaff machines.

The idea is quite simple. A moving belt of insulating material passes round two pulleys, one near floor level and one some forty or fifty feet above, the height depending on the voltage and the length of spark required. (See illustration on page 18.)

An electric motor drives the lower pulley so that the belt passes up to the top and down again continuously. The belt and all the driving equipment, together with the bottom and top pulleys, are enclosed in a tubular insulating structure which is closed at the upper end by a large metal sphere.

As the belt leaves the lower pulley on its way upward, and again as it approaches the upper pulley, it passes near a series of sharp metallic points. The lower points are connected to an electric generator which gives a voltage of several thousand volts. This is sufficient to cause the points to discharge onto the belt as it passes. The charge so collected travels upward on the moving belt until it comes opposite the upper series of points. Again,

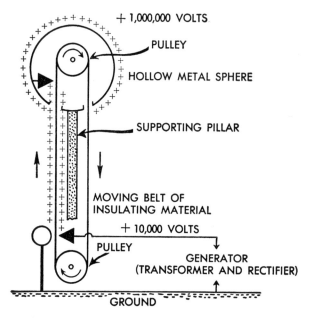

+ 1,000,000 VOLTS

PULLEY

HOLLOW METAL SPHERE

SUPPORTING PILLAR

MOVING BELT OF
INSULATING MATERIAL

+ 10,000 VOLTS

PULLEY

GENERATOR
(TRANSFORMER AND RECTIFIER)

GROUND

Van de Graaff generator. A potential from an electric machine is taken to a point near the lower part of the rising belt. The charge is sprayed onto the belt and is carried up and inside the top collecting sphere. Here it is transferred to the outside surface and the discharged belt passes down to the lower pulley to collect a further charge.

owing to the point effect, these pick up the charge and pass it to the large surrounding sphere. The belt continues, discharged, on its way around the upper pulley and back to the lower one. The sphere acts as a Faraday cage and in this way its charge is built up until enormous voltages are available, capable of producing lightninglike flashes of thirty feet or more through the air.

When men first started to produce static discharge by means of frictional and influence machines, they soon recognized in the appearance and noise of the spark the close similarity to lightning and thunder. Benjamin Franklin was fascinated by the subject and gave much time and thought to studying lightning phenomena and relating them to experimental laboratory discharges under controlled conditions with such condensers as the Leyden jar.

Great risks were taken at this time by Franklin and others in attempts to control lightning, A French scientist erected an iron rod on his house forty feet high in 1752 and drew sparks from the lower end when thunderclouds passed over. One similar experimenter in Russia was even more successful and was killed by such a discharge. The story of Franklin's experiment with a kite to which he fixed a sharp-pointed wire is well known. To the lower end of the twine holding the kite he attached a key and tied a few feet of silk ribbon. Franklin wrote that when a thundercloud passed over and the string became wet "so as to conduct the electric fire freely you will find it stream out plentifully from the key on the approach of your knuckle. At this key the phial [the Leyden jar] may be charged; and from the electric fire thus obtained spirits may be kindled, and all the other electric experiments be performed which are usually done by the help of a rubbed globe or tube and thereby the sameness of the electric matter with that of lightning completely demonstrated."

You may well be advised to try many of the experiments described in this book, but do not experiment with kites in thunderstorms. It is much too dangerous. Also, while on the subject, watch your step when flying kites near power lines; this can be equally risky.

We must not let this account of the early adventurers pass without a word of thanks to them for the protection we get for our large buildings today through the lightning conductor. By means of a strip of copper an inch or more wide and one eighth of an inch thick or a heavy braided cable, we collect the static charge at the pointed upper end and so conduct the dangerous condition safely and quickly to the ground.

When a building not provided with a lightning rod is struck by lightning, the heavy discharge current may cause explosions at places where there is moisture, as in brick, stone, or wooden parts, so breaking up the fabric and setting fire to combustible materials. The lightning rod may drain away the charge before it builds up to such a dangerous extent but, even if it is unable to prevent a direct stroke, the current passing through the metallic circuit is much less likely to result in explosion or fire. The worst that may happen is that the rod may become heated, but if it is designed generously this will not be serious.

Although we cannot carry out our own experiments with lightning, there is no reason whatever why we should not have a clear understanding of what happens in a flash of lightning. Many recent experiments have been carried out under safe conditions and we now have a fairly good picture of the process. By sending up small balloons carrying recording apparatus, we know the distribution of electric charges in a thundercloud and the temperatures at different points. By modern high-speed photography we know the usual characteristics of the flash and, by many measurements, the magnitude of the electrical quantities involved.

A thundercloud may reach several miles in height and be six to eight miles long. The lower part of the cloud, usually a thousand to fifteen hundred feet above the ground, is charged negatively and the upper part is charged positively. The temperature of the greater part of the cloud seems to be below the freezing point and is lowest in the upper parts. As there are violent upward air currents in the cloud, it would appear that the separation of the electricity into positive and negative is due to the impact of ice particles on one another. The same thing happens during blizzards in polar regions and, in a different form, in dust storms.

It would be expected from the distribution of charges between the upper and lower part of a cloud that the most usual type of lightning flash is within the cloud. A smaller proportion of the flashes occurs between the cloud and the earth. For every flash to earth, there may be as many as five or even ten within the cloud. The ones that interest us, of course, are those that pass between the earth and clouds, and it is estimated that something like one hundred such flashes occur every second all the year round.

In tornadoes, lightning is very violent. There may be as many as twenty flashes per second, and some of the sparks are ten miles long. It has been calculated that in the famous Massachusetts tornado of 1953 the power generated was equal to the output of all the power stations in the United States, or to the power of an atom bomb dropped every three minutes.

It is estimated that there are about sixteen million thunderstorms over the earth every year, and nearly two thousand going on at the same time.

The noise of thunder is due, of course, to the heating of the air as the lightning flashes through it, and the subsequent collapse on cooling. Knowing the speed of sound in air to be 1100 feet per second, we can calculate the distance of a lightning flash by taking the time between seeing the flash and hearing the thunder. The flash is over in a fraction of a second but the resulting thunder may rumble on for many seconds. This is due to the fact that some parts of the flash are much farther from us than others and the sound takes longer to reach us.

CHAPTER *2*

Magnetism

THE story of electricity is intimately bound up with the subject of magnetism. We have already observed how early man saw the beginnings of electricity in the form of static electricity. In the same way, many centuries ago, people noticed certain curious things which opened up the way to a knowledge of magnetism. What they did not see, however, was the essential connection between electricity and magnetism which we have come to know only during the past two hundred years or so.

Indeed it may be said that modern electrical engineering rests entirely on the combination of the two. It is as though two great streams of thought had come down side by side through the ages like two rivers, and suddenly joined together in the eighteenth century through the discoveries of men of science. Electricity and magnetism grew independently. Hundreds of years ago they were known quite separately, even in the mind of the same man. For instance Dr. William Gilbert of Colchester, England, whose work on magnetism we shall read about later, had no idea of the fundamental connection between electricity and magnetism, though he appears to have demonstrated both electricity and magnetism to Elizabeth I of England.

The beginnings of a knowledge of magnetism are shrouded in mystery, although references appear quite early in the history of mankind. Thales of Miletus spoke of the attraction of magnets six centuries before Christ. The Chinese at an even earlier date are said to have used what were called south-seeking carts. These vehicles, which took them in a southerly direction, could only have been directed by some magnetic device.

Early magnets were either lodestones or pieces of iron magnetized by being rubbed with a lodestone. Lodestone was a natural mineral found in a place called Magnesia, in Asia Minor, and thus the word magnet originated. The substance is an oxide of iron called *magnetite* or magnetic oxide of iron; its chemical formula is Fe_3O_4.

When a piece of lodestone was hung in a container by means of a fine thread so as to be in a horizontal position, it was found to set itself in a north and south direction. This peculiarity gave the substance its name—lodestone, or leading stone. It became, in fact, a compass.

The most usual forms of permanent magnet are the bar magnet and the horseshoe magnet, but it is only the bar magnet which is useful as a compass to indicate the north and south direction. The reasons for this we shall see. All magnets have poles. Peter Peregrinus pointed out in 1269 that there were two regions, or poles, near the ends of a magnet where the magnetism appeared to be located. He noticed that, when the magnet was suspended, one of the poles always tended to move toward the north and the other toward the south. The end which tends to point toward the north pole of the earth he called the north pole of the magnet and the other end the south pole.

If we take a bar magnet and sprinkle iron filings over it, we find that the filings do not stick at the center of the magnet but mostly at the ends, the effect tailing off toward the center. Again, we see the effect of the two poles. (See illustration on page 24.)

In addition to noticing the way in which a suspended magnet would line up with the north-south direction of the earth, Peter

When a bar magnet is dipped into a mass of iron filings, they stick to it, principally near the two ends where the poles of the magnet are.

Peregrinus also described how the north magnetic poles would repel one another, as would two south magnetic poles, but when a north pole and a south pole were brought near one another, attraction took place.

Float a small bar magnet in a wooden boat on a saucer of water. Notice that, when left to itself, it will gradually move round and will set itself north and south. If we bring up the north pole of a larger magnet and offer it to the north pole of the floating one, the latter moves away. The south pole of the floating magnet on the other hand will immediately move toward the north pole of the large magnet.

The explanation of these phenomena was given in 1600 by Dr. William Gilbert. For twenty years Gilbert studied these various effects and looked up all the early writing on the subject. He then wrote a great book called *De Magnete* which proved to be of the highest importance. Although the fact that the floating or suspended magnet turned north and south had been known for hundreds of years, nobody knew why. Gilbert gave the answer: the earth itself is a magnet!

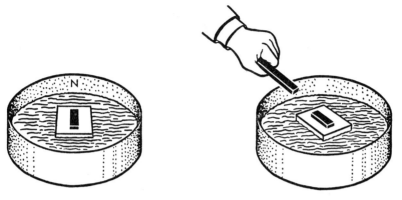

Small magnetized bar floating in a small boat on a basin of water lies in a direction north and south unless disturbed. The approach of a second magnet causes it to rotate.

It seemed strange that a globe could be a magnet with magnetic poles; one usually thinks of a magnet's being a bar-shaped object. But Gilbert made an iron ball and magnetized it by rubbing it with a lodestone, and it acted exactly like the earth. It had north and south poles. But there was one difficulty. A north pole was known to reject a north pole, but the north pole of the earth attracted the north pole of the magnet. Gilbert overcame this by calling the end of a suspended magnet which turned toward

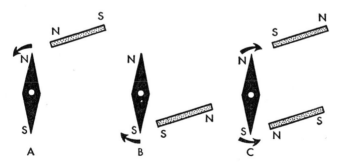

(A) *One north pole rejects another north pole.* (B) *One south pole rejects another south pole.* (C) *North and south poles attract each other.*

the north the *north-seeking pole* and not the north pole; that convention still applies today. The north-seeking pole is really a south pole in comparison with the north pole of the earth.

Gilbert's experiments also took notice of another important feature in terrestrial magnetism known as *dip*. If we were to go to the equator and balance a bar magnet by a thread at the center and then carry it carefully to Canada, we should find that it would no longer be balanced but that the north-seeking end would dip considerably from the horizontal. The angle in Canada would be 75° to 80°. On the other hand, if we carried the balanced magnet down through South America, we should observe that it would be the south-seeking end which would dip and that

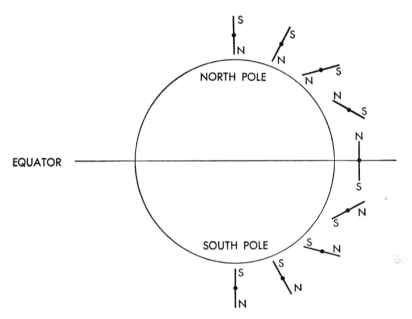

A perfectly balanced compass needle dips from the horizontal, and the amount of the dip depends on the distance from the equator. In the northern hemisphere the north pole of the needle dips increasingly as the needle is carried north, and in the southern hemisphere the south pole dips increasingly as the needle is carried south.

it gradually would dip more and more as we approached Cape Horn. There it would lie at an angle of about 60° with the horizontal—the so-called angle of dip which is about 70° at New York and about 60° at Houston, Texas. When carried to the magnetic north and south poles of the earth, the magnet would turn completely vertical; at the north pole the north-seeking end downward and at the south pole the south-seeking end downward. The angle of dip at the north pole is 90° and at the south pole minus 90°.

To show this magnetic dip the magnet must be supported at its center of gravity so that apart from magnetic attraction it is perfectly balanced.

In a piece of apparatus known as the *dip circle,* corrections can be made to overcome any unbalance in the weight of the magnet. The dip is an indication of the direction of what we call the magnetic field from the point on the earth's surface where we make our test.

We have now introduced a new word, *field,* or *magnetic field,* and the best way to understand the idea is to make an experiment.

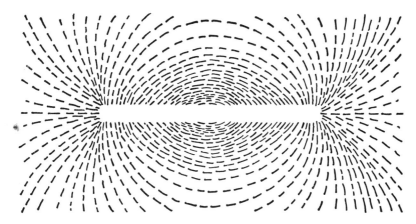

Picture of the lines of magnetic force obtained by sprinkling iron filings on a card lying on a bar magnet.

Place a small bar magnet on a wooden table and lay over it a stiff sheet of paper. Then sprinkle a spoonful of iron filings over the paper, tapping the paper gently from time to time with a pencil. (You can find a few filings under the bench vise in a workshop or garage, but get iron filings and not brass.) The filings line themselves up in a most interesting pattern. They make a kind of map of lines, all of which leave one pole of the magnet and travel in a wide sweep to the other pole. You have made a picture of the magnetic field in the space around the magnet.

Every magnet possesses such a field, and the shape will depend on the shape of the magnet and the proximity of other magnets or pieces of magnetic material. Place a piece of soft iron, such as a large nail, near the end of your magnet and make another picture. You will see that the field is drawn out in the direction of the nail. We speak of the lines of force as traveling from the north pole of the magnet through the air and back to the south pole. These lines are rearranged by the presence of the nail, which draws them to itself.

There are many combinations of magnet and magnet, or magnet and pieces of iron which you can experiment with, and it is a worthwhile occupation to make a small collection of the resulting fields, shapes, or patterns of lines of force. This can conveniently be done by using wax paper. Sprinkle the filings on the wax paper, and while they are in position, warm the paper from above with a hot object such as an electric iron. This will fix the filings in position on the paper so that you can remove the paper from the magnet without losing the pattern.

We can form a good idea of the mechanism of the forces between magnets—attraction between unlike poles, and repulsion between like poles—by studying the magnetic fields between magnets. When two bar magnets are laid side by side, the north end of one opposite the south end of the other, the lines seem eager to rush across and form a link between the two magnets at both poles. The magnets welcome each other, as it were, and, if suspended or laid on a smooth slippery surface, they will move across to make contact with each other.

On the other hand, when similar poles are opposite each other, they move away. The shape of the field in this case explains why: the lines avoid each other. Those from magnet *A* would much sooner go out into the air and travel quite a long way to get back home again than have anything to do with the lines of magnet *B*. And magnet *B* feels exactly the same about it.

When we were discussing electrostatics in chapter 1 we saw that charges of static electricity could be induced in a body. In a similar way magnetism can be induced by placing a magnet near a piece of soft iron. A horseshoe magnet, such as that used for moving the little iron indicator in a maximum-minimum thermometer in a greenhouse, has lines of force leaving one pole and entering the other just as they do in a bar magnet. In this case, however, the distance from pole to pole being small, the field is intense and the lines of force do not have to travel a great distance through the air. To assist in retaining full strength in a horseshoe magnet a piece of soft iron is usually kept attached to the pole pieces. This is called a *keeper*.

You will understand why a horseshoe magnet attracts the keeper if you lay the magnet and the keeper a little distance apart on the table and make a filings picture. If they tend to close together, put a match between to keep them apart. The lines of force leave the north pole of the magnet, enter one end of the keeper, travel the short distance to the other end and then jump the gap back to the south pole. Where lines of force leave iron, we have a north pole; where they enter iron, we have a south pole. Thus the end of the soft iron keeper adjoining the north pole of the magnet becomes a south pole, and unlike poles attract one another.

Similarly, at the other end of the keeper the lines are leaving and so form a north pole. While the keeper, made of soft iron, may show no signs of magnetism when remote from the magnet, it becomes a magnet temporarily when placed near the magnet poles with the result that the lines of force can pass through it. In the same way, if we hold a bar magnet vertically and attach a soft iron nail to its lower end, the nail becomes temporarily a magnet and will pick up a second nail at its lower end.

A toy called the *magnetic mummy* depends on this phenomenon. A bar magnet made of a specially powerful magnetic steel is made up with plastic to look like a mummy. It fits into a sarcophagus, in the base of which is concealed a similar magnet. When the mummy is laid in the sarcophagus with its north end over the south end of the lower magnet, all is peace and the lid can be closed. If you hand the mummy to your friend the wrong way round and ask him to put it to sleep he just can't get it to lie down. If he forces it, the lid is thrust open and out pops the mummy again. In fact, the force of repulsion is so great that the mummy will remain poised in the air between the sides of the casket in the position in which like poles are adjacent.

The mummy magnet is made of a very powerful type of steel. Although permanent magnets have in the past usually been made of ordinary carbon steel, very important developments have taken place in recent years to produce more powerful magnets by mixing other metals with iron. When cobalt, nickel, aluminum, tungsten, and some other of the rarer metals are alloyed with iron, the magnetic properties can be improved many times. This is a big field of study. Hundreds of thousands of permanent magnets are used in various electrical appliances. One well-known example is the electricity meter, and there are many others which require exceptional properties. The result is that scientists are continually investigating the subject of magnetic steels and improving the performance of permanent magnets.

So far, in this chapter on magnetism, we have not mentioned

that most important practical application—the ship's compass. We have discussed attraction and repulsion of unlike and like poles and have shown that the earth is virtually a large magnet with north and south poles. We have also seen that a permanent bar magnet when suspended by a thread or floated on water will automatically turn itself in the direction of the surrounding magnetic field.

Peter Peregrinus of Picardy described the use of a compass in the thirteenth century, although the principle had even then been known for hundreds of years. But it was less than a hundred years ago that a famous British scientist, Lord Kelvin, made the ship's compass an instrument of precision. Kelvin divided the compass needle into eight small needles supported side by side by silk thread below an aluminum disk. The weight was taken by a central sapphire cap on a pivot tipped with the hard metal iridium.

For navigation at sea it is not sufficient to know merely which is the north and south direction but it is necessary to know also the direction in which the ship is heading. This is indicated by the compass card, a disk marked with the points of the compass. First of all, the four main points N, E, S, and W are shown, the N having a decorative fleur-de-lis. Between them are spaced NE, SE, SW, NW; and again, between these eight, another eight, the NNE, ENE, ESE, SSE, SSW, WSW, WNW, and NNW points. A further set again between these, but unnamed, gives the compass a total of thirty-two points. For increased precision there is a still further addition of four subdivisions per point, but the modern compass has also gradations in degrees from 0° at N around to 360° at N. The direction in which the ship is heading is indicated by the number of degrees opposite a mark, called the lubber's point, in the fixed case. For instance, when the ship is traveling due north the lubber's point is at 0°. When traveling due east, it is at 90°; and when traveling southwest, the reading is

225°. The card remains correctly pointing north and the lubber's point moves round with the ship.

When you go on a ship you may have an opportunity to look in the binnacle, the supporting pillar about four feet high, carrying the compass. There, looking through the sloping window, you will see the device used for keeping the compass card and its bowl horizontal no matter how the ship rolls or pitches. It is known as a gimbal and consists of a ring surrounding the compass, pivoted at opposite sides, while the compass is again pivoted inside the ring on pivots at right angles to the outside pivots. If you have played with a gyrotop, you will understand the arrangement.

In a refinement of the ship's compass for battleships, where the shock of gun fire would interfere with the ordinary dry compass, the compass is floated in a liquid, a mixture of water and alcohol. There is a central pivot, as in the dry compass just described, but the float takes most of the weight of the moving parts and there is thus very little load on the pivot.

When you are inspecting a ship's binnacle you may notice certain large lumps of iron attached to the outside, two in the shape of balls and one a stout vertical rod. These are to correct the effect of temporary magnetization of the ship's hull by the earth's field as she swings round on different courses. There is also a permanent magnetization of the hull acquired during the building of the ship. This is corrected by placing a number of permanent magnets on the binnacle below the compass, with their poles pointing in the opposite direction to that of the ship's magnetism.

To ensure that these various corrective devices are effective, a series of tests is carried out before the ship goes to sea. The process called *swinging the ship* consists of mooring the ship to a buoy and moving it in turn through the points of the compass.

When we talk of the earth's being a magnet, we must explain

that the magnetic north pole is not at geographic or true north, but many miles from it, and is constantly though slowly moving. For this reason mariners have to take into account what is called the *declination,* or variation, which is the deviation of the compass away from true north. This may amount to several degrees and varies in different parts of the world, but charts are available and the navigator can correct his position by referring to them.

It is not surprising, in view of the fickle nature of terrestrial magnetism, that inventors have sought an alternative to the magnetic compass, and today all the largest vessels are equipped with the gyrocompass, which depends on the principle that when a heavy body is spun at a high speed it tends to retain the same axis of rotation. The gyrocompass is a very complicated and expensive device and there are still many ships using the magnetic compass.

CHAPTER 3

The Electric Current

IN Chapters 1 and 2 we discussed static electricity and magnetism. These two subjects are the very basis and beginning of our knowledge of the electrical world, but we cannot light our homes by rubbing a glass rod, nor can we run the vacuum cleaner with a bar magnet. A vast amount of discovery and invention has had to be built up on these fundamental ideas before we could enjoy all the wonderful applications of electricity which make up our daily life. So let us now direct ourselves toward more practical matters.

A striking feature in the use of electricity in the various devices we employ is the steady flow—the electric *current*. From the moment we switch on the lamp, the electric stove, the vacuum cleaner, or whatever it is, the current continues to flow until we switch it off again. The important thing is to maintain the current.

The earliest known form of electric current is the lightning flash when the charge, gradually built up in a storm cloud, is suddenly released and travels as a current to another cloud or to the earth. In this case the current is of a very short duration, less than one one-hundredth of a second, and so far as continuous supply for domestic and industrial purposes is concerned it is quite useless. The magnitude of the current in a lightning flash is enormous, something like 20,000 to 100,000 times that which is used in our 100-watt light bulb. It is not continuous, however, but lasts for only a fraction of a second.

The steady, continuous electric current came to us as the discovery of one man. Before the year 1800 there was no such thing; then an Italian scientist, named Alessandro Volta, carried out a series of experiments which startled the scientific world and gave us for the first time this inestimable boon.

Volta was a professor in the University of Pavia, a man of good family, well traveled, and a friend of scientists in many countries. He was born in 1745 in Como, Italy. During his life he made an enduring contribution to human progress in a most remarkable series of scientific investigations. He had a wonderful and unusual gift for experimentation and carried out some astonishingly sensitive electrical measurements with the simplest of apparatus. His electrometer, for instance, made of two straws which repelled one another when charged, was famous for a long time until it was superseded by the gold-leaf electrometer. By a most ingenious device he increased the sensitivity of this instrument in the following manner. He made a condenser of two metal plates, the upper one being coated with a thin layer of varnish and provided with an insulating handle. He connected this condenser to the electrometer while the latter was being charged and then separated the plates by lifting the top one by its handle. Thus, as the capacity of the subsidiary condenser was reduced to practically zero, its charge flowed into the gold leaves and so magnified the effect. This principle of increasing sensitivity has since been adopted by many investigators.

Among Volta's important inventions was the electrophorus, which was the forerunner of the static induction machine and of a host of other ingenious and effective instruments.

In 1795, when the victorious Napoleon Bonaparte entered Italy with his army, Volta was a member of the delegation which met him. When, at the age of fifty-four, he wished to retire from his professorship, it was Napoleon who said: "I cannot agree to Volta's resignation. If his activities as professor are too great a burden they must be limited. He may give even only one lecture a year but the University of Pavia would be wounded to the heart if I were to allow so famous a name to be struck off the rolls of its members!" Consequently Volta remained at the university until the last few years of his life. He died at the age of eighty-two. A visit to Como today is an inspiration to any student of electrical science. Volta's name has been handsomely honored by the erection of a beautiful building, the Temple of Volta, in which many of the original items of equipment made and used by him are preserved. And further, as a worthy and romantic tribute to the great man whose work brought us the electric current, a powerful electric light flashes out every night high up in the mountains above his birthplace to tell his fame to all.

So much for Volta the man. Now what was the famous experiment that gave us for the first time the continuous electric current? I have said that the important date was 1800 but the foundations for the great discovery were laid a few years before by another Italian scientist, Luigi Galvani, a professor of medicine at the University of Bologna. How often it happens that one man works in a field of knowledge and produces ideas which open up completely new vistas far beyond his own capacity to explore, but which start off an important train of thought in another man's brain. So it was in this case. Galvani did something which set Volta to thinking and this is how it happened.

Galvani was studying the nerves of frogs which controlled the movement of their limbs. It was already known that electric shocks could cause contraction of living muscle, but Galvani began a careful research on dead frogs. In the year 1780 one of those remarkable accidents happened which sometimes reward the scientific investigator. Galvani was dissecting the leg of a dead frog while someone was operating an electrical machine some distance away. Suddenly he saw the dead leg jump.

Because he was a wise and painstaking experimenter, Galvani saw at once the significance of the discovery. For eleven years he carried out hundreds of experiments, observing new and important phenomena, all of which he described in 1791 in an essay called "The Force of Electricity on the Motion of Muscles." In this essay Galvani, in addition to describing the effect of the remote electric machine already referred to, described how the twitchings of frogs' legs occurred in the open air during thunderstorms.

He then made an observation, the subsequent results of which were most important. When a frog's leg was attached by a brass hook to an iron fence, and the leg was blown by the wind into contact with the fence, contraction of the muscle took place even on a clear day, with no lightning about and no electric machine in operation. Here was something quite new. Galvani repeated the conditions indoors and with different metal connecting the nerve and muscle of the leg. Some of the conclusions he reached were right. For instance, he said that the effect was stronger with some metals than with others, and this is true; but we now know that one of his ideas was wrong. He decided that the contraction was due to electricity generated in the frog and gave it the name "animal electricity." It became known also as Galvani's electricity. A few years later, in 1798, Galvani died at the age of sixty-one.

On hearing of Galvani's experiments, Volta became interested in them. After he tried out the ideas in his own laboratory, he arrived at the conclusion that the electricity had not come from the animal tissues but from the metals in contact. He also observed, in one of his reports on the subject, that a sensation could be obtained by a living person from the same cause, and if you wish you may try out Volta's simple experiment on yourself.

Take a small strip of copper about ¼ inch wide and 2 inches long and a similar strip of zinc. While keeping the ends apart, place one strip on the tongue and the other below the tongue lightly touching. Now bring the outer ends into contact with one another and you will immediately feel the sensation of sourness or taste of metal due to the current passing through your tongue.

Thus, after conducting this experiment, Volta concluded, quite correctly, that the origin of the electricity which caused the effects on the frogs' legs was in the contact of dissimilar metals, and he carried out a large number of tests with different pairs of metals. First by means of the tongue test, and then with the electrometer, he placed the various metals in order and the series became known as the *voltaic series*. At one end stands zinc and at the other carbon, while copper is somewhere between.

In addition to the definite order of metals in this sense Volta observed another important fact: the zinc becomes charged positively; that is, it exhibits the same kind of electricity as that obtained by rubbing a glass rod in the static experiments, while any other metal lower down in the voltaic series becomes negative. Thus when a piece of copper is in contact with a piece of zinc, that face of the copper which is remote from the point of contact with the zinc becomes negative. Similarly, the face of the zinc remote from the point of contact with the copper becomes positive. When copper is in contact with carbon, the copper is positive and the carbon negative. A metal is always positive toward another metal lower in the series.

Volta next discovered how to increase the effect and constructed what has become the world-famous voltaic pile, in which small disks of zinc and copper are placed one above the other, the pairs being separated by disks of moistened cardboard or other fibrous materials. So he built a many-decker sandwich of zinc, copper, cardboard; zinc, copper, cardboard; and so on. He found that he could produce a considerable voltage

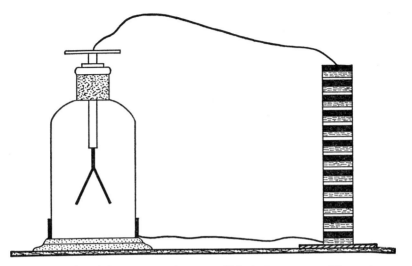

Volta's pile (right) *connected to a gold-leaf electroscope. The series of couples of dissimilar metals separated by moistened fabric generates a voltage sufficient to cause the leaves of the electroscope to repel one another.*

between the upper and lower plates and could draw off a current which to all intents was unending. By using brine or weak acid to moisten the fibrous disks, he still further increased the effect.

Volta's great discovery was announced by him in 1800 in a paper to the Royal Society in London and the following is an extract from the *Philosophical Transactions* published at that time:

> *A Come en Milanois*
> *ce 20me Mars 1800.*
>
> Après un long silence, dont je ne chercherai pas à m'éxcuser, j'ai le plaisir de vous communiquer, Monsieur, et par votre moyen à la Société Royale, quelques resultats frappants auxquels je suis arrivé, en poursuivant mes expériences sur l'électricité excitée par le simple contact mutuel des metaux de differente espèce, et même par celui des autres conducteurs, aussi different entre eux. . . .

He goes on:

> Yes, the apparatus of which I am telling you, and which will doubtless astonish you, is nothing but a collection of good conductors of different kinds arranged in a certain manner. 30, 40, 60 pieces, or more of copper, or better of silver, each laid upon a piece of tin, or, what is much better, zinc, and an equal number of layers of water, or of some other humour which is a better conductor than plain water, such as salt water, lye etc., or pieces of cardboard, leather etc., well soaked with these humours: such layers interposed between each couple or combination of different metals, such an alternative succession, and always in the same order of these three kinds of conductors, that is all that constitutes my new instrument, which imitate, as I have said, the effects of Leyden jars, or of electric batteries, giving the same shocks, as they do; which in truth, remains much below the activity of the said batteries charged to a high degree, as regards the force and noise of the explosions, the sparks, and the distance over which the discharge can take place etc., only equalling the effects of a battery charged to a very low degree, of a battery having an immense capacity, but which besides, infinitely surpasses the virtue and power of these same batteries, inasmuch as it does not need, as they do, to be charged beforehand, by means of outside electricity; and inasmuch as it is capable of giving a shock whenever it is touched however frequently these contacts are made.

In the same paper Volta goes on to describe the *couronne des tasses* (crown of cups), a series of small cups containing brine or weak acid into which were dipped connecting strips of zinc and copper all arranged "in series"—that is, one after the other —the conductors not touching each other in the cup but connected together between cups. Volta's original *couronne des tasses* is still preserved with all the other interesting relics in the museum at Como.

Volta's announcement of his discovery created a great stir in the world of science, and all eyes were directed to this wonderful electric current which he had presented. Scientists were anxious to study its properties to see what were its effects, and for that purpose attention was early paid to producing it in more powerful forms. Quite quickly—in fact, within a few months of Volta's paper to the Royal Society—two Englishmen, Nicholson and Carlisle, performed an experiment with two brass wires connected to a voltaic pile which they had made. When the wires came into contact with water, they noticed that bubbles of gas appeared on the surface of one of the wires, though not on both. The other wire turned a dull tarnished color. The gas was hydrogen and would burn when collected and ignited. When they used platinum wires instead of brass they saw that gas collected on both wires, hydrogen on one and oxygen on the other. Very soon it was noticed that there was twice as much hydrogen as oxygen, and it became clear that they had decomposed water (H_2O) electrically for the first time into its components, hydrogen (H) and oxygen (O). Today the process is called *electrolysis.*

The first man to seize onto the electric current and to explore the new field of science which it opened up in a satisfactory way was Humphry Davy, the young professor at the Royal Institution of London. He was born in 1778 at Penzance, in Cornwall, England, the eldest of five, where he enjoyed much idleness at the grammar school and seems to have been considerably in advance intellectually of his schoolmaster. He was witty and had a vivid imagination and a love of poetry. He had a remarkably sympathetic and understanding mother. Her stock of stories and readings from books developed a facility for storytelling in the young Humphry, which resulted in his becoming a mature orator and a leader among his schoolmates at a very early age. When no live audience was present he would stand on a chair and make eloquent speeches to an imaginary one.

Apprenticed to an apothecary on leaving school, Davy continued to develop a strong and energetic personality. He studied mathematics and chemistry and took to experimenting in the attic of the house of his guardian. While still a youth Davy had the flair for choosing valuable friends; the son of Watt, the famous engineer, was one, and Gilbert, later a president of the Royal Society, another. With their help he was appointed at the early age of twenty assistant to the Pneumatic Institute at Bristol—a curious organization for curing people of their ailments by the administration of gases.

The young man found himself in a well-equipped laboratory, and he continued his scientific studies in the new surroundings with enthusiasm. One of his achievements was to try the effect of laughing gas by making himself unconscious.

About this time Count Rumford, a remarkable American living in England, took a prominent part in the foundation of the Royal Institution. When the post of director became vacant Davy was appointed in 1801 and, although young, was a brilliant success from the start. At a bound he became famous for his scientific lectures, and fashionable London flocked to hear him. His eloquence is said to have been so remarkable that Coleridge the poet was among the audience "not so much to receive scientific instruction as to increase his stock of metaphors."

Davy's contributions in the field of heat and vacuum were of great importance. Our particular interest, however, is the contribution he made to the progress of the electric current. In the electrolysis of water he showed that the two gases, oxygen and hydrogen, could be collected in two separate containers inverted over the two electrodes and submerged in the liquid. He built a large battery on the lines of Volta's *couronne des tasses,* but with 200 pairs of zinc and copper plates having a total surface area of 12,800 square inches. With this powerful tool he made a number of far-reaching and fundamental discoveries.

His first really dramatic discovery was the electric arc. When the terminals of a battery are brought into contact with one another and then separated, a spark appears at the point of contact. Davy found that by separating the wires from his battery a short distance apart the sparking continued across the gap with intense light and heat. After experimenting with different metals he used carbon rods and so produced the beautiful dazzling electric arc. He gave it the name "arc" because, when the carbons were opposed to one another in the horizontal direction, the stream of light and heat took on the form of an upward bow, or arc. This was due to the rising air currents.

The discovery of the carbon arc opened up great possibilities, one of which was electric light. Never before had there been such a bright light produced artificially, and the result was that for many years electric arc lamps were used extensively for illumination. Today, except in a few very special situations, the arc lamp has given place to the filament lamp and even more modern forms of lighting.

In another field Davy's discovery is still of great value. He observed the intense heat generated in the arc and on the carbon tips, which became white hot. In particular, the positive carbon developed a crater, or cup, on its tip; and the depth of this crater was found to be the brightest and hottest part of the assembly. When placed in this crater, all metals were liquefied, even platinum, while precious stones like sapphires and diamonds seemed to evaporate. We shall see, when we come to chapter 8, how the modern electric furnace developed from Davy's discovery, and what a valuable tool it is today in certain industrial fields, especially for smelting aluminum and iron.

After studying the decomposition of water by the electric current Davy turned his attention to the effect of passing the current through other substances, in particular potash and soda, in which he had been interested for some time. They had always been considered as elements, but here was a new way to test the matter. He would see what happened when he passed the electric current through them. Consequently he heated some potash in a platinum spoon until it was liquid and then connected the two poles of his powerful battery, the positive one to the spoon and the negative one to a wire dipping into the potash. At once the liquid became agitated around the wire; and, after a little bubbling, bright silverlike globules rose to the surface and burst into flame.

We read that Davy's delight when he saw the tiny shining globules like mercury bursting through the crust of potash and taking fire as they reached the air was so great that he could not contain his joy; he bounded about the room in ecstasy. And no wonder, for he had produced a new element. For the first time in history potassium had been isolated. This metal has such an affinity for oxygen that, when exposed to the air, it bursts into flame.

Davy's success in isolating potassium led him to test other undecomposed substances, and in a short space of time he had not only isolated sodium, calcium, strontium, barium, and magnesium, but had made a detailed study of many of their properties.

With all these new and astonishing phenomena to lecture about —the voltaic battery, the carbon arc, and the remarkable new materials which he had brought to light—Davy brought great credit to the Royal Institution and established its reputation for all time as the birthplace of electrical science.

When experimenters, following Volta's discovery, began to realize the great value of the current provided by the pile and *couronne des tasses,* they needed larger currents. Davy and others quickly found that the original proposals, while containing the idea, had to be modified considerably to give the strong currents required. At first they increased the size of the metal plates immersed in acid and the size of the cup. The arrangement became known as an *electric cell,* or battery, and much ingenuity

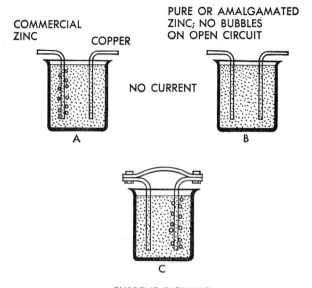

COMMERCIAL ZINC

COPPER

PURE OR AMALGAMATED ZINC; NO BUBBLES ON OPEN CIRCUIT

NO CURRENT

A

B

C

CURRENT FLOWING

Simple electric cell. Two plates, one zinc and one copper, dip into weak sulfuric acid. (A) Cell on open circuit, with commercial zinc. Hydrogen escapes at negative plate. (B) Cell on open circuit, with amalgamated zinc. No gas is freed. (C) Cell, with amalgamated zinc, in use. No hydrogen is freed at zinc plate, but hydrogen is produced at positive plate, calling for a depolarizer.

has been displayed over the years in improving this device which has assumed such an importance in modern life.

The simple cell consists of two rods or plates, sometimes called *electrodes,* which dip into dilute sulfuric acid, known as the *electrolyte.* Various metals may be used for the electrodes but zinc and copper are suitable. One electrode (the copper) is said to be positive and the other (the zinc) negative. When these conventions for positive and negative were first adopted, based on the type of electricity generated by friction on glass and other substances, the electron was not known. It became the fashion to speak of the positive pole being the source of the current and to picture the current flowing out of the positive pole of the battery through the circuit and back to the negative pole. This convention still holds widely and we often refer to the current flowing in this direction, although we know that movement within the circuit is the movement of electrons from the negative pole through the circuit back to the positive pole.

Now when such a simple cell begins to give out a current, tiny bubbles of gas collect on the surface of the copper plate down in the electrolyte. Presently an almost continuous coating of hydrogen gas is formed and this naturally reduces the contact of the metal plate with the acid. The result is that the current coming from the cell dies off and the cell becomes useless. If we remove the bubbles of gas by brushing the plate, the original conditions are restored and the current returns to its full value, but obviously such a procedure would have to be repeated frequently and would therefore be tedious and impracticable. This effect is called *polarization*.

There is another defect of the simple cell which must be referred to. This is known as *local action*. Polarization of the copper plate starts only when the cell is used and the current begins to flow, but local action goes on all the time whether the cell is in use or not. Local action takes place at the zinc electrode and is due to impurities in the zinc.

As we have seen, the generation of current in an electric cell is due to two plates of different metals in acid. If the zinc plate contains impurities—say, for example, tiny specks of copper— then each little speck of copper in contact with the surrounding zinc as well as with the acid contributes a current. But this local current just goes around and around, eating up the zinc and contributing nothing to the outside circuit. Local action commences as soon as the zinc electrode is immersed in the acid, so the cell may be completely exhausted even before it is taken into use for supplying current.

What are the answers to polarization and local action? In local action all we need to do is to use very pure zinc instead of zinc with bits of iron, arsenic, or other impurities embedded in it; or alternatively we may amalgamate the zinc. This also is simple and quite usual. Mercury alloys itself easily with zinc, so that coating the zinc with mercury amalgam completely defeats the impurities which are trying to make trouble. In modern cells the amalgamated zinc rod stands in the electrolyte for years and does not disappear within a few days as it did formerly.

Defense against polarization, however, is not so simple and many different methods have been tried. Only two need be discussed, as they typify the principles involved. The Daniell cell invented in 1836, now only of academic interest, had zinc and copper electrodes, the zinc in the form of a rod and the copper comprising the containing vessel. The zinc stood in the acid electrolyte in an inner porous pot and the outer space held a solution of copper sulfate for mixing but it allowed the current to pass. When the gas bubbles—hydrogen ions we call them at this stage—tried to pass so as to deposit themselves on the copper container, they were cleverly replaced by copper ions in the outer solution. The hydrogen went harmlessly and quietly into the solution and copper was equally conveniently deposited on the copper container. In this way the current could be taken for long periods without serious diminution of strength.

Another early type of cell specially designed to overcome polarization, and which did veteran service for many years, was the Leclanché cell. In this cell the electrodes were zinc and carbon and the electrolyte a solution of ammonium chloride, often called sal ammoniac. The zinc rod, amalgamated of course, stood in the solution in an outer glass container and the carbon rod or plate was packed inside an inner porous pot with a black powder. This powder was the depolarizer and consisted of a mixture of manganese dioxide and powdered carbon. The action in this case can be described simply.

When the current flowed, the electrolyte, ammonium chloride, split up; and the ammonium carrying the dangerous hydrogen passed through into the porous pot. Here the hydrogen was seized by the manganese dioxide defending the carbon plate so that, again, no gas could collect on the positive carbon electrode and the battery continued to operate successfully.

A Leclanché cell could supply current for quite an appreciable time, though the cell did require periods of rest to enable the depolarizing action to take place. For this reason the Leclanché cell was used for such intermittent service as operating electric bells and telephones. It had the advantage of being cheap and required only the addition of water now and then to keep it going for years. Its chief interest today is that it was the original cell which led to the modern dry cell used so extensively.

There are many situations today where a portable source of current is required. When the necessary strength is not too great the dry cell is used. These cells are made in various forms, particularly for flashlights and radio sets. The dry cell is really a Leclanché cell, so constructed that the electrolyte will not spill. The zinc electrode in this cell forms the container. The carbon rod is packed in a paste made up of the depolarizer contained in a sack of fibrous material. The electrolyte is again in the form of a paste, filling the space between the sack and the zinc case. A chemical, zinc chloride, is added to both pastes to prevent the cell from becoming too dry, and special refinements are introduced in some dry cells to take care of gas escape and to prevent deterioration during storage.

The cells just described are not suitable for providing heavy currents, and for this purpose we use what are known as *secondary* cells, sometimes called storage cells or batteries or accumulators. Because of their appearance in every automobile they are well known. These secondary cells are valuable sources of electric current.

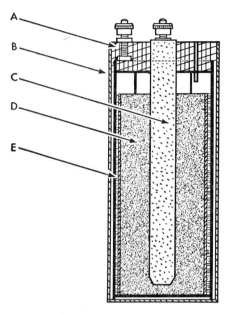

Commercial dry cell, showing construction to prevent polarization.
(A) Negative terminal. (B) Container. (C) Carbon rod electrode.
(D) Paste electrolyte. (E) Zinc electrode.

Many attempts have been made by scientists to explain the flow of electricity, or electric conduction, but the explanations are complicated and difficult to understand. We shall see, as we study electrical effects, that current will pass through solid objects, through liquids, and through gases. For this the electron is responsible.

When the current flows in a metallic wire, we notice that the wire is heated. In the wires that supply the light in our homes the heating is not very apparent; in the elements of domestic electrical equipment the heating is very real. In the filament of the incandescent bulb the heating is very intense. We know also that, when the current flows through a liquid, it produces certain definite effects, such as decomposition of the liquid and pro-

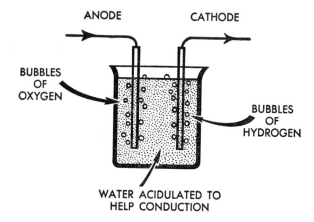

ANODE   CATHODE

BUBBLES
OF
OXYGEN

BUBBLES
OF
HYDROGEN

WATER ACIDULATED TO
HELP CONDUCTION

Simple electrolytic cell. Two metallic electrodes immersed in dilute acid (electrolyte). Current enters by the anode and leaves by the cathode.

duction of bubbles. When it flows through the air, as in Davy's arc or in lightning, it produces light *and* heat. In all these different media—solid, liquid, or gas—there must be something going on!

It is convenient to defer an intimate study of the electron until we come to a later chapter and to consider at this stage what happens when a current flows through a liquid. Fortunately in a liquid carrying a current we can see much of what is going on. Take the simplest of all experiments, current passed through dilute acid between two immersed plates. The setup, consisting of container, weak acid, and immersed plates, is known as an *electrolytic* cell. The acid is the electrolyte, the two plates the electrodes, and what goes on is called *electrolysis*. The plate, or electrode, by which the current enters an electrolytic cell is the anode, and that by which it leaves is the cathode.

If we connect a primary battery to such an electrolytic cell, the current leaves the positive pole of the battery—the copper or carbon plate in the case of a primary battery—and enters the electrolytic cell by the anode. After leaving by the cathode, the current returns to the negative pole of the battery. It is desirable, when carrying out this experiment with primary cells, to use several connected head and tail, or, as we say, *in series*. One cell is not sufficient to overcome a natural opposition which is experienced in all electrolytic cells. Also, to simplify the process, use platinum plates in the electrolytic cell.

The current should now be passing through the electrolyte from the platinum anode to the platinum cathode. Immediately bubbles of gas form at the surface of each electrode and rise to the top. There appears to be more coming from the cathode than from the anode. Because electricity is an exact science we must measure the amounts, so let us place two inverted liquid-filled measuring tubes over the electrodes and catch the gases coming off. Gradually the gases are collected and, when we have sufficient, we note the markings on the tubes. The cathode has given off exactly twice as much gas as the anode. (See illustration on page 52.)

When we apply a glowing splinter and open the cock of the anode tube the splinter bursts into flame; we have prepared oxygen. When we apply a match to the slightly opened cock in the cathode tube we see that the escaping gas itself burns with a steady flame; it is hydrogen. Electrolysis has produced two volumes of hydrogen (H) and one volume of oxygen (O). We have decomposed water, H_2O, into its constituent gases. (Note that I have called the electrolyte weak acid and not water; it was almost entirely water with just a few drops of sulfuric acid added to help the current to pass through. Pure water has a high resistance to the flow of current and a few impurities help.)

If we cover both electrodes with one tube and collect all the gas, we shall of course have a mixture of hydrogen and oxygen; and, as the proportions are correct for combination, it is explosive; when ignited, it becomes water again. An interesting experiment consists of smearing a soap solution on the outlet of the tube and blowing a bubble with the mixture of gases. Putting a lighted taper to this bubble produces a loud explosion. In this experiment it is desirable to use a longer glass tube to obtain the necessary gas pressure to blow the bubble.

These simple experiments show that the current decomposes water into its constituent gases. If we now use as electrolyte a solution of blue crystals of copper sulfate and allow the current to flow, we find something quite different happening. No bubbles of gas appear this time but the cathode quickly becomes covered with a thin coating of copper. Similarly if another chemical, silver nitrate, is used for the electrolyte, the cathode becomes coated with silver. The current picks up the particular metal concerned and carries it to the cathode in the same way that it car-

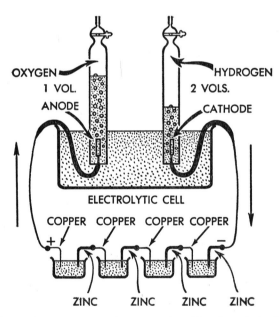

Collection and measurement of gases produced by electrolysis. Oxygen at the anode and hydrogen at the cathode. Note that the volume of hydrogen is twice that of the oxygen.

ried the hydrogen in the first experiment. How are we to measure the current?

The early pioneers soon found the need for measuring current, and indeed for a unit of measure. You can't measure a pound of nails or a yard of dress material until you have agreed on what you mean by a pound and a yard. These everyday units have been settled and laid down a long time and are, in fact, defined by law. The same need for standards applies in electrical quantities and the unit of current is a very important unit. In considering electrolysis and the deposition of substances in an electrolyte we have a very exact method of measuring current and defining the unit. We know, for instance, that if we deposit silver at the rate of 0.001118 gram per second we have a current of one *ampere*. That is how an ampere is defined legally. There are not different kinds of ampere. Wherever you go in the world you will find the same ampere; it always deposits silver at the rate of 0.001118 gram per second.

The ampere always releases hydrogen gas at the rate of 0.00009355 gram per second. With the electrolytic cell and two collecting tubes you can check this figure quite easily. Hydrogen does not weigh much, so the tiny weight of 0.00009355 gram means quite an appreciable volume. In fact, as you will be measuring volume, I will work it out for you. A current of one ampere will generate hydrogen at the rate of 0.1165 cubic centimeter per second (slight corrections for temperature and barometric reading at the time of the experiment). Your tube should be marked in cubic centimeters so that in 100 seconds one ampere will give you a measurable volume of hydrogen of 11.65 cubic centimeters. One-tenth of an ampere would produce the same volume in just over a quarter of an hour.

The process of electrodeposition of metals has become important in industry. Inexpensive knives, spoons, and forks are made of a cheaper metal, such as nickel, and then are coated by electrolysis with pure silver. Many articles in common use, such as automobile parts, bicycle handle bars, bathroom fittings, etc., are plated by this process and many different metals are used for the purpose.

Sometimes worn parts of machinery are restored to their original usefulness by having further metal deposited electrolytically on them. Copies of complicated articles can also be made by this process. A mold of the article is made by pressing into it a soft waxlike substance which is then stripped off, dusted over with a conducting material to carry the current, and plated with copper or other metal. This in turn can be stripped off the mold and will form an exact replica of the original object.

Another application of electrolysis to electrodeposition is in connection with the manufacture of records. The sound is recorded on the face of the disc in a groove which starts at the outside and gradually moves in along a slow spiral toward the center. For recording, a stylus, operated by fluctuations in sound pressure created by the voice or music, moves backward and forward across the groove on the original wax disc. From this original recording large numbers of copies are made, and it is in the making of these duplicates that the electrolytic process is employed.

First the surface of the original disc is coated with an atomized film of gold, then a fairly heavy coating of copper is plated on in an electrolytic bath. This metal is stripped off as a negative: it has characteristics opposite to those of the original plates; for, where the original sound wave caused a ridge, the negative will have a hollow. If the stripped disc is now pressed onto a disc of the material of which the final record is to be made, it will correctly produce the original and the pressed disc can be used for playing on a record player.

Among the many extensive industries based on the use of the current in electrolysis is the production of aluminum. The raw alumina, an oxide of aluminum, is separated by various mechanical and chemical processes from all the other clays and rocks and then treated in a steel container, or bath, which has a thick carbon lining. This carbon acts as a cathode and the anode is a carbon rod. When a heavy current is passed from the upper rod to the carbon container, the aluminum separates as a pure metal, collects in the bottom of the bath, and at intervals is drawn off and cast into molds. To make a ton of aluminum requires the expenditure of 20,000 kilowatt-hours, or units, of electricity; that is, 20,000 times the consumption in a 1,000-watt electric stove in one hour. For this reason aluminum is usually refined near hydroelectric stations where power is cheap.

By similar methods zinc, copper, and other metals are refined by electric current on a large scale. A wide range of chemicals is also produced electrically; chlorine, for instance, is made from common salt by passing a current through a brine solution. Similarly, the production of the raw materials for soaps, rayon, detergents, and a host of other products frequently depends on electrolysis. In these various plants enormous currents of tens of thousands of amperes are used.

Another important use of electrolysis is in the secondary cell. A secondary cell is an electrolytic cell so constructed that the changes which the current produces enable it to produce its own current in a reverse direction when the original current is discontinued. The electricity is not actually stored as we store electricity in a static condenser, but it is converted into the form of chemical energy by a reversible process.

Let us construct again a simple electrolytic cell with dilute sulfuric acid as electrolyte. We will use two strips of lead for the anode and the cathode. Exactly as before, when we pass a current into the anode and out the cathode, oxygen and hydrogen are separated. This time, however, we notice that, while hydrogen appears as bubbles on the cathode, no oxygen bubbles appear on the anode. The oxygen is certainly there, for we observe that the surface of the lead turns brown in color; this discoloration is due to a deposit of lead peroxide. The oxygen on formation has combined at once with the lead to make the peroxide.

We have made a rudimentary secondary cell and charged it. If we disconnect the charging current and connect the plates to a pea bulb, we now get a small return current. This soon dies off, however, and at the same time the appearance of the electrodes changes again; they both assume a grayish white color due to a coating of lead sulfate. A further charge from the primary battery causes the lead sulfate at the cathode (negative plate) to disappear, and clean lead appears once more in its place, while at the anode (positive plate) the lead peroxide appears again. This process of charging and discharging can be repeated indefinitely.

These four formulas show what happens when the cell has settled down after several charges and discharges:

During charge

At the positive plate (anode) the lead sulfate disappears and lead peroxide appears.

$$PbSO_4 + SO_4 + 2H_2O \rightarrow PbO_2 + 2H_2SO_4$$

At the negative plate (cathode) the lead sulfate disappears and plain lead appears.

$$PbSO_4 + H_2 \rightarrow Pb + H_2SO_4$$

During discharge

At the positive plate (anode) the lead peroxide disappears and is replaced by sulfate.

$$PbO_2 + H_2 + H_2SO_4 \rightarrow PbSO_4 + 2H_2O$$

At the negative plate (cathode) the plain lead becomes coated with sulfate.

$$Pb + SO_4 \rightarrow PbSO_4$$

When the man at the garage checks your battery, he looks to

see whether the density of the battery acid is too low. The formulas show you why. During discharge, sulfuric acid is replaced by water so that the density, or specific gravity, falls. Testing the specific gravity is a check on the state of the battery.

In practical secondary cells the construction of the plates is much more complicated than that of our simple cell. To ensure a high storage capacity, the plates are made porous, or in the form of grids, so as to expose the maximum surface to the acid. In one cell there are usually groups of interleaved plates kept apart by glass rod, wood, or ebonite separators, the outside plates always being negative.

But what really goes on when the current passes through a liquid? We have seen quite a lot through the effects which are visible. We said earlier that the electron was an active participator, and much thought has been given to studying its share in the

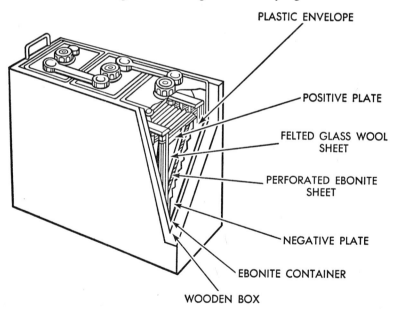

PLASTIC ENVELOPE

POSITIVE PLATE

FELTED GLASS WOOL SHEET

PERFORATED EBONITE SHEET

NEGATIVE PLATE

EBONITE CONTAINER

WOODEN BOX

Storage battery, or accumulator, with three cells. Side cut away to show plates.

various processes. As a result of this consideration and many measurements which have been made by hundreds of scientists, we have today a fairly reliable picture of this unseen world.

The current through an electrolyte is pictured as being carried by electrically charged particles of matter called *ions*. Some ions carry negative charges and, since they move toward the anode, they are called *anions;* the others, carrying positive charges, move toward the cathode and are called *cations*. Pure water does not conduct electricity easily because its constituent molecules remain intact. When we add small amounts of certain other substances to water, they go into solution, that is, all the separate molecules of the substance become individually surrounded by water molecules and they become ionized—their electric charge is separated into two parts.

If we imagine that a molecule of sulfuric acid is egg shaped, when it is dissolved in water it becomes ionized and it breaks into two half eggs. Chemically we say the complete acid molecule is H_2SO_4; and, on being ionized, the H_2 forms one half egg and the SO_4 the other. Under the influence of the charging current the H_2 goes to the cathode and the SO_4 to the anode. What we actually detect at the anode is, however, only oxygen, which is released from the SO_4, the remnant combining with the solution. The action at the electrode itself, as in the case of the secondary cell, is very important.

An illustration of this is the action of the electric plating bath with two copper electrodes and an electrolyte of copper sulfate. The molecule of copper sulfate is represented by its chemical formula $CuSO_4$. When this is dissolved, the components are copper, Cu^+, and the item known as the radical SO_4^-. These are the ions. The copper ion is charged positively and shown thus, Cu^+, because, being positive, it goes to the negative pole. The remainder of the molecule, the SO_4^-, is charged negatively and travels to the positive pole.

When the cations of copper arrive at the cathode, they discharge themselves and supply the current of electricity for the external circuit, remaining attached to the plate in the form of a new coating of copper. When the anions of the radical SO_4^- reach the anode, they seize onto atoms of copper in the metal plate, give up their charge, and form new molecules of $CuSO_4$. These molecules then take their chance of surviving dissociation in the general melee throughout the solution but ultimately, no doubt, succumb and continue to repeat the process. The upshot is that copper is corroded from the anode and deposited or plated onto the cathode.

A revolutionary development in electric batteries has taken place recently in what is known as the fuel cell invented by Bacon, an Englishman. Instead of consuming a metal in an electrolyte, the Bacon cell consumes the gas hydrogen.

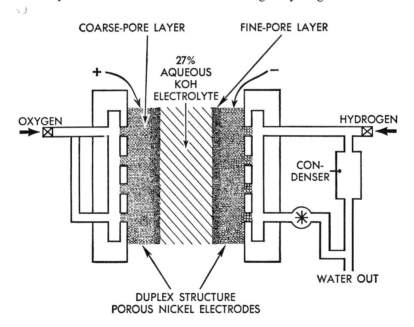

The Bacon fuel cell. (Adapted from The New Scientist)

Hollow flat plate electrodes of nickel-plated steel are used and one side is drilled with a large number of small holes. This side is then coated with layers of porous nickel, coarse grains near the plate followed by finer ones on the outside. Gas is then pumped into the hollow plates—hydrogen into one and oxygen into the other—and it finds its way slowly through the powder to the surface.

The two plates are immersed in a solution of caustic potash in water and the action which takes place can be represented by the following formulas:

At the oxygen plate, the water and the oxygen gas combine in this way to produce charged ions:

$$H^+ \cdot OH^- \ + \quad O^2 \quad \rightarrow \quad OH^- + OH^-$$
$$\text{(water)} \qquad \text{(oxygen)} \qquad \text{(negative ions)}$$

These negative ions move about in the electrolyte and ultimately come into contact with the hydrogen gas at the other electrode. Here the following combination occurs:

$$OH^- \qquad + \qquad H^+ \qquad \rightarrow H^+ \cdot OH^-$$
$$\text{(negative ion)} \qquad \text{(hydrogen)} \qquad \text{(water)}$$

As the ions move across, they carry a negative charge and so generate a potential of about 1 volt, which can then be used for driving a current through an external circuit.

In order to produce the necessary action with the hydrogen, the pressure and temperature have to be raised so that a number of these thin cells are assembled in a strong container—head and tail fashion like the early voltaic pile. In the first commercial cells a pressure of 400 to 600 pounds per square inch and a temperature of 200° C have been adopted and a unit of 40 cells, each ten inches in diameter and about half an inch thick, gives an output of several kilowatts.

It may be a long time before the fuel cell replaces the lead and other forms of battery but it appears already to be an interesting competitor and may even provide alternative methods of producing electricity on a large scale to help meet our growing needs for energy.

This chapter has covered only the most elementary explanation of the underlying principles of electrolysis and how the current travels through a liquid. The process is a very complicated one, much more so than the simple experiments in this chapter would lead one to believe.

CHAPTER 4

The Path of the Current

A GREAT part of the work of the electrical engineer consists in designing and constructing the path along which the current will flow and in preventing any deviation from that path. The current must be led from the point where it is generated to the place where it is to be used. It must be correctly carried inside the apparatus from one point to another. We must be in a position to stop or start the current at will and to regulate the strength, while nothing must be permitted to interfere with the flow.

The various paths along which electric currents flow are numerous. The difference between one kind of path and another may be illustrated by comparing the heavy bus bars in a power station with the slight tinsel conductor in a telephone cord, or the steel-reinforced aluminum conductors carried across the country on steel towers with the complex wiring of a radio set.

Probably the most fundamental fact about an electric path is that it *conducts* electricity, and that it must be *insulated* from other objects. The early experimenters with static electricity soon made the discovery about insulation; they used silk threads, varnished surfaces, and glass handles to prevent leakage of the electric charge from metal parts. Today insulators are made of a wide range of substances including porcelain, rubber, mica, paper, and oil. For insulators exposed to the weather, porcelain is widely used, and the corrugated supports for high-voltage outdoor power lines or the smaller pots carrying telephone wires are well known. The air itself is a relatively good insulator, hence an outdoor line need be specially insulated only at the points of support. An underground or submarine cable on the other hand must be insulated along its entire length, otherwise the conductor would come in contact with the ground. Similarly, the wiring in a building or throughout an automobile must be insulated to keep it out of contact with other objects.

The path along which the current flows is known as the *circuit*. It may be a simple "go" and "return" or it may be a complicated arrangement of conductors and insulators. A peep into a radio set will give you an idea of what is meant by the modern term *circuitry,* and the harness of wiring used in an airplane is a wonderful example of electrical design and construction.

When connecting a number of separate pieces of electrical equipment we can employ two fundamentally different methods. We can connect the items either in *series* or in *parallel* (see page 64). In series, the same current passes through them all in turn, one after another. Objects connected in parallel take their current individually and are independent of one another. A good example of series connection is in the automobile battery. The cells are connected by heavy lead lugs, positive to negative, one after another. Parallel working is evident on all hands: the lamps in a house are all in parallel with one another, and the connections of the different houses to the cables in a street are again in parallel with one another. Sometimes a combination of series-parallel connection is employed, and again the automobile furnishes a good example: while the current passes through the cells in series, it goes to the lamps individually in parallel. On certain railroad motors a series-parallel method of starting up is adopted: the motors are first switched in series with one another;

and, when the train is approaching full speed, they are put in parallel.

Two circuit features which often control the flow of electric current are the *open* circuit and the *short* circuit. In the open circuit the current stops because of a discontinuity in the conductor; it may be caused by a dirty contact in a switch or wire terminal, or it may be due to the blowing of a fuse. A short circuit results when the two wires from the source of supply are brought into contact with one another, as for instance in a badly wired lamp where the covering of the wires has been trimmed too far back. Dropping a wrench across the terminal of a secondary battery produces a very obvious kind of short circuit. When trouble is experienced in the operation of electrical equipment, we should first of all look for an open circuit and then for a short circuit.

Because of the possible serious effects of short circuits, electrical systems are carefully protected by *fuses,* or cutouts, which in the emergency "blow" and disconnect everything. The short circuit thus automatically introduces an open circuit which, while

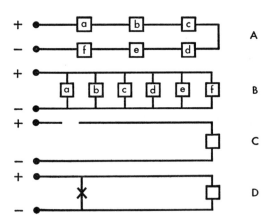

Circuit components in series and parallel. (A) Six elements—cells, instruments, machines, etc.—connected in series. (B) The same in parallel. (C) An open circuit. (D) A short circuit.

stopping everything, is less likely to cause fire or personal harm.

Two important points must be watched, therefore, for a circuit to operate successfully. In no place must there be a disconnection —a soldered joint must not be badly made, the contacts in an electric bell or in the distributor on an automobile must be clean, the fuse wire must not be loose in its holder, the brushes in a small motor must be rubbing on a clean commutator, and so on. An experienced electrician knows where to look for all these defects which can have such important consequences; a disconnection anywhere in the circuit stops the current throughout the circuit.

The short circuit, on the other hand, may be caused by wires touching one another unintentionally, by water soaking the equipment, by a nail driven in carelessly, or by a wire thrown over bare conductors. The short circuit provides the current with an easy return path to the source of supply rather than the more arduous one we prepare for it. To prevent short circuits we take every possible precaution to maintain the insulation of the live conductors by avoiding mechanical damage and false connection and by preventing the ingress of moisture.

The circuit embraces everything through which the current passes; and, although this is usually a metallic wire or rod of some kind, there are many important items through which current is made to flow which are not wires. For example, we have already spoken of the electric arc in which the current jumps from carbon rod to carbon rod, and of the electrolytic cell where it travels by ionic conduction in a liquid. We shall see further in chapter 11 that in radio and such branches of science a very important component of a circuit may be a glass tube containing a vacuum, or for some types of electric lamp even one containing special gas. For the present, however, it will be best to restrict our consideration to metallic circuits and to learn what we can about them before we come to gaseous circuits.

A circuit must be designed for the current it has to carry. A small wire may be quite suitable for carrying the tiny currents of the telephone circuit. These are measured in milliamperes. A milliampere is a thousandth part of an ampere. Even tinier currents are sometimes used in scientific work and these may be measured in microamperes, millionths of an ampere. A house circuit to supply several electric heaters may carry ten amperes or more; and the third rail on an electric railway, several thousands of amperes. The heavier the current the larger the conductor necessary.

It is not only the dimensions of a conductor which determine its current-carrying capacity. The nature of the metal is important, as a simple experiment will show. Suppose we take a number of pieces of iron and copper wire of the same size, each a few inches long, and join them together, alternately iron and copper. After stringing up the composite length between two supports, we will pass a current through them. With a small current we should not notice much difference between the iron and the copper; but, as we increase the current, we find that the iron becomes warm while the copper remains cold. Further increase in the current makes the iron hot, and the section of iron wire may even be brought up to incandescence while the intermediate copper section remains only warm and dull.

To ensure the most efficient transmission of electricity, therefore, we select for our conductors the metal that keeps cool in use. If price were no consideration, silver would be very suitable, for it conducts eight times as well as iron; but the most popular metal for the purpose is copper, which is nearly as good as silver and much cheaper.

During the past few years the price of copper has risen so much that for many electrical purposes its pre-eminent position is threatened by another metal—aluminum, particularly for outdoor overhead conductors where weight is also a factor.

In discussing this ability of different conductors to carry a current of electricity, we speak of their electrical resistance. It is as though there was some internal opposition to the flow. Silver and copper offer a low resistance; iron offers a high resistance. A thin wire offers a high resistance in comparison with a thick wire of the same metal. Although copper as a metal is a better conductor than iron, a hundred feet of thin copper wire may have a higher amount of resistance than a hundred feet of thick iron wire.

Different metals have different values for their qualities of *resistance*. With this new quantity, electrical resistance, we introduce a new unit of measurement. It is called the *ohm,* after a German scientist of that name. Ohm's law is the basis for calculating the current in a circuit. The value of resistance of electrical copper is known. Here it is in a practical form:

> A wire 1000 feet long and 1-square-inch
> cross section has a resistance of 0.008 ohm.

With this information you can calculate the resistance of any copper wire of any length and size. If it is twice as long as the standard, that is, 2000 feet, and the same cross section, the resistance will be twice 0.008, or 0.016 ohm. If, on the other hand, it is only one one-hundredth of a square inch in cross section, the resistance will be 100 times 0.008, or 0.8 ohm.

There are certain refinements on all these calculations. For instance, the resistance of the copper wire varies slightly with the temperature. The standard value of 0.008 ohm for 1000 feet of 1-square-inch rod is true only at a temperature of 60° F, and a temperature coefficient has to be used to calculate the value at other temperatures.

You know that a current of so many amperes is required for a certain purpose, and you may have a known power supply and perhaps a length of wire to carry the current to the point where you want to use it. How do you decide whether the current will be sufficient for the purpose? Ohm's law shows that current is proportional to the voltage in a circuit and inversely proportional to the resistance. Expressed as a formula it is this:

$$\text{current (amperes)} = \frac{\text{voltage (volts)}}{\text{resistance (ohms)}}.$$

Suppose we had a secondary cell which would maintain a voltage of 1.6 volts at its terminal when giving current. If we connected, across the terminals, a length of copper wire 2000 feet long and $\frac{1}{1000}$ square inch in cross section, wound into a coil, what would the current through the wire be?

First we must calculate the resistance of the wire on the basis of the standard just given. It would be twice as much because of the increased length, and a thousand times as much because of the reduced cross section. Thus the resistance would be 2000 times 0.008, or 16 ohms. If we apply Ohm's law, the current through the wire would be 1.6 volts divided by 16 ohms. As a formula this is:

$$\frac{1.6}{16} = \frac{1}{10} \text{ ampere.}$$

The matter of voltage is very fundamental. The voltage in a circuit is the original force which pushes the current along. Sometimes it is called *electromotive force* (emf) and sometimes *potential difference* (pd) and it is measured in volts.

The voltage of a primary cell is about 1.5 volts, depending on the particular materials used in construction. Secondary cells have a voltage of about 2 volts, which falls away during discharge. The usual voltage available on the wiring in our homes is 120 volts, while some transmission lines carry current long distances at 230,000 volts. In connection with testing and special application of high-voltage electricity, figures of ten million are reached. For convenience in speaking of these very high voltages we employ *mega*volts (millions of volts), *kilo*volts (thousands of volts), and in very low voltages—such as those used in radio or generated by the human heart—*micro*volts (millionths of a volt).

The contemplation of an accidental shock of 10,000,000 volts might make a difference in my heart flutter of 0.000001 volt; but such a situation could be expressed more easily as the effect of a possible 10MV shock being 1 microvolt.

When we apply Ohm's law we must be sure that we have the whole of the resistance of the circuit. We might make this mistake for instance: with a cell as a source of supply we could measure its voltage on open circuit before starting—that is, its emf—and forget that the cell itself has internal resistance. When we connect an external circuit to the terminals of the cell, some of the emf is used up in overcoming the internal resistance of the cell and the actual voltage at the terminal falls. For convenience we call the voltage that is available at the terminal the potential difference (pd), so if we use the value of the pd in our formula we can also use the resistance of the external circuit. It is this pd that is sending the current through the external circuit in which we are interested. It must be measured while the current is flowing after part of the open-circuit emf has been deducted in overcoming the internal resistance of the cell.

It is confusing to apply Ohm's law when there is a *back* emf in the circuit. If we have three cells pushing the current in one direction and two cells connected in opposition so that they are pushing the current in the opposite direction, the current will go in the direction decided by the three cells, and the real voltage available for pushing the current is only that equivalent to one cell. That is why it was important, in charging the simple electrolytic cell in chapter 3, to use more than one primary cell in order to overcome the back emf of the cell that was being charged.

If you try to charge a secondary cell which has a voltage of 2 volts with a 1.5-volt dry cell, the secondary cell, instead of being charged, will discharge itself back through the dry cell. But join two dry cells in series, then their total voltage will be 3 volts and the opposition of the secondary cell's 2 volts will be overcome. In this case the effective voltage to use for applying Ohm's law to the circuit is $3 - 2 = 1$ volt, and the resistance is the combined resistance of the two dry cells and the secondary cell— that is, the total resistance in the circuit. The resistance of the connecting wires should, of course, also be added.

Let us look at the interior of the metallic conductor and try to understand how the current passes through. The electron is responsible in all three conductors of electricity—solids, liquids, and gases. The electron has a very active relationship with the anions and the cations in liquids. Where does it help in the solid metallic conductors?

All matter is made up of tiny particles called atoms. A rough estimate of the diameter of an atom is one hundred-millionth of an inch and for many years atoms were considered the smallest possible subdivisions of matter. Today we know that the atom is in itself a complex system embracing a nucleus surrounded by

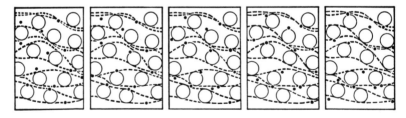

How a current of electricity travels along inside a conductor. The electrons normally spinning around individual atoms become detached and drift along under the influence of the voltage, as can be seen by inspecting the five successive pictures.

electrons which spin around it continuously in different orbits. One nucleus may have different numbers of electrons, depending on the particular element. The gas hydrogen for instance has only one electron, carbon has 6, copper 29, and uranium 92. The nucleus of an atom is electrically positive and the electrons are units of negative electricity. Normally the number of electrons in an atom is such that their total negative charge balances the positive charge on the nucleus. Electrons, however, can be detached or added. When one of the electrons is removed, the balance is upset and the atom becomes positive. When an extra electron is added the atom becomes negative.

Small as is an atom, its component nucleus and the revolving electrons are many thousands of times smaller still, so it is true to say that even a solid object is not really solid but consists of millions of tiny objects floating in space. It has been pointed out that, if we eliminated all the unfilled space in a man's body and collected into one mass the electrical particles of which it is composed, the man would be reduced to a speck just visible with a magnifying glass.

Turning to our metallic conductor, then, we can imagine a space in which atoms are widely separated, each with its tenuous cloud of spinning electrons.

From our earlier study of electrostatics we know that a negative charge subject to an electric field tends to move: "like" poles repel; "unlike" poles attract. The negative charge is pushed away from the negative pole of the imposed field and toward the positive pole. In our conductor, filled with these electrons moving about like fireflies, a potential difference introduced by connecting a cell to the two ends will cause the electrons, being negative, to drift toward the positive pole. This does not mean that they will rush straight to the pole; for, in their progress in between the millions of atoms, they suffer many hazards. They travel at enormous speeds for short distances but they keep changing their direction. Their average speed along the conductor amounts to only a few inches an hour. Although the speed of the electron is so slow and the charge on each one so tiny, powerful currents as are now commonly used are possible because of the vast number of electrons carrying the current. It is estimated that in a 100-watt bulb there are something like six million million million (or 6×10^{18}) electrons passing through the filament every second.

In chapter 3 we talked of the current leaving the positive copper and going around the circuit back to the negative zinc. The early history of electricity was tied up with the polarity of rubbed rods and at that stage there was no inconsistency, for in those days nobody knew about the electron. That was discovered less than sixty years ago, and I have just shown you that in a conductor the current is carried by millions of electrons which are negative.

In the secondary cell the anion moved in the electrolyte toward the positive pole, though carrying a negative ion. The current, then, does not really move from positive to negative but from negative to positive. This seems inconsistent, but when a negative thing moves in one direction it is really the same thing as a positive one going in the opposite direction.

If I take a glass tube of colored water with a bubble in it and raise one end with my right hand, the bubble rises and passes from my left to my right hand. The real movement in the tube is in the opposite direction; to allow the bubble to pass from my left hand to my right the water in the tube has to pass in the opposite direction, from my right hand toward my left. In electrical circuits, although we know that the actual carriers of the electricity travel from negative to positive, we continue the convention that the current flows from the positive to the negative, the positive pole having a higher potential than the negative pole does.

No description of the electrical circuit would be complete without a reference to a particular circuit which is used not so much for conveying the current from place to place but as a device in electrical testing. This circuit is known as the Wheatstone bridge, named after Professor Wheatstone of King's College, London. It consists of four parts connected together in diamond formation; and these components, *A, B, C,* and *D* are known as the arms of the bridge. If a cell is connected to *P* and *Q,* two of the corners of the diamond, and an instrument for detecting current, called a galvanometer, to the other corners, *R* and *S,* we can make some very important measurements of the values of the resistances of the arms *A, B, C,* and *D.* If we adjust these values by varying the length of wire or by other means until the galvanometer shows no deflection, an important relationship is established:

$$\frac{A}{B} = \frac{C}{D}.$$

The Wheatstone bridge is used for determining the unknown resistance of a wire, *A.* The values of two of the arms, *B* and *D,* are known, and *C* is a resistance that can be varied. *C* is adjusted until the galvanometer shows no current through it, and under

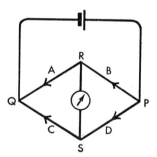

The Wheatstone bridge. A connection of four conductors A, B, C, and D in a diamond formation is shown. Current is fed into the bridge at two opposite points, P and Q. A galvanometer is connected across the two remaining points.

these conditions the value of the unknown resistance is given be-low:

$$A = \frac{BC}{D}.$$

As an example suppose we take two coils of wire, each 100 ohms, and insert them at B and D. We then adjust C; and, if the value to bring the galvanometer to zero is 300 ohms, the value of the unknown A will be:

$$A = \frac{100 \times 300}{100} = 300 \text{ ohms.}$$

The arms B and D need not be alike. Say B is 10 ohms and D 50 ohms, and the balancing resistance C is 250 ohms, then A is given by:

$$A = \frac{10 \times 250}{50} = 50 \text{ ohms.}$$

The control of the electric current in a circuit is very impor-tant. In the first place switches are required for connecting and disconnecting at will; and many different designs are used, de-pending on the magnitude of the current, the voltage of the circuit, and the situation. Probably a bell push is as simple a switch as can be found. It consists of two pieces of springy metal with screws for connecting the wires to the circuit so that nor-mally they are not in contact. Pressure from a small knob brings the springy contacts together, completing the circuit and allow-ing the current to pass.

At the opposite extreme of importance and complexity are the large, high-voltage circuit breakers used in bulk-supply trans-mission systems. The problem in these is to extinguish the vicious discharge and arcing which takes place when conductors carry-ing heavy currents at high voltage are separated. If the arc were not suppressed quickly, it would burn up the contacts and probably fuse the parts together so that no disconnection could be made. An accidental short circuit on a system must be disconnected immediately, otherwise the heavy currents would ruin the generating machine in the powerhouse and probably cause risk to human life. Two main principles are employed in these switches. In one the arc is blown out automatically by a blast

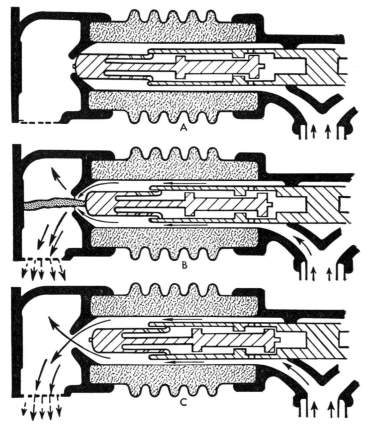

A circuit breaker, a type of electric switch used for large power circuits. This is an air-blast breaker, in which a powerful blast of air blows out the arc at the contacts when the switch is opened. (A) Contacts closed. (B) Contact partially opened; arc forming; air blast commencing. (C) Contacts fully opened; arc extinguished. (Adapted from Metropolitan-Vickers Electrical Co. Ltd.)

of compressed air at the moment the contacts are separated, while in the other the parts are all immersed in a tank of insulating oil which prevents or extinguishes the arc automatically. These are called air-break and oil-break switches respectively.

In between these extremes of the bell press button and the heavy circuit breakers is a large range of switches used for controlling circuits of all kinds. In the home, lighting switches may have various mechanisms that move a piece of metal in and out between two fixed pieces provided with flexible contacts. These switches might be operated by a *tumbler* knob, by *on* and *off* press buttons on a wall panel, or by a cord to the switch in the ceiling. On electric ranges we are accustomed to the rotary two- or three-heat switches which have four contacts and are so connected to two heating elements as to connect only one or to place both in series or in parallel.

In many items of electrical equipment automatic switches are employed. The large circuit breakers already referred to are so built as to be released automatically when the current reaches a dangerous value, and on most motor circuits in industrial plants there is similar provision of overload trips.

A well-known example of an automatic switch which operates continuously is found in every automobile. It is the distributor, which connects the ignition current in turn to the spark plugs on the different cylinders. A circular case of insulating material carries four or more stationary contacts which are connected by thickly insulated wires to the spark plugs. Inside the case a rotating key-shaped arm comes opposite the different contacts in turn and the current jumps across at the correct moment. The circuit in this case starts from the ignition coil, jumps from the rotor to the appropriate contact, then goes through the cable to the center conductor of the spark plug. Here the current flashes across the gap between the plug points, igniting the gases in the cylinder, and then passes back to the coil. (There is also a switching device known as a "make and break," but this will be explained in connection with the electric bell later in chapter 5.)

In many electric circuits it is necessary not only to start and stop the current at will by the use of switches, but to vary the amount of current flowing. Although there are various ways of doing this, the most usual one is by inserting into the circuit a variable resistance. According to Ohm's law, if we have a source of supply giving a particular voltage, the current in the circuit will depend on the value of the resistance. We may not be able to alter the value of the resistance of the item we are supplying with current—a motor, for instance—but we can insert additional resistance in series with the motor. The form of this additional resistance depends on the service it is to perform. In a laboratory, for instance, a coil of many feet of bare or varnished iron or alloy wire is wound on a cylinder and a sliding contact rubbing on the turns, bared where necessary by scraping, includes more or less of the length as desired.

Industrial motor starters often have a series of coils of resistance wire mounted in a metal box. The coils are connected in series, but the end of each coil is connected to a brass contact. These contacts are arranged in a circular row mounted on a panel of slate or other insulating material on the front of the box. An arm carrying a spring contact sliding over these fixed contacts can be moved at will by a handle. At the "off" position the arm does not make contact and the motor is not connected to the supply. When moved one notch it meets the first fixed contact and connects the motor through all the resistance coils. As the motor speeds up, the arm is moved slowly over the contacts one by one, cutting out coil after coil; when it has reached its final position, there is no resistance in the circuit and the motor is running at full speed connected directly to the supply line. (See illustration on page 78.)

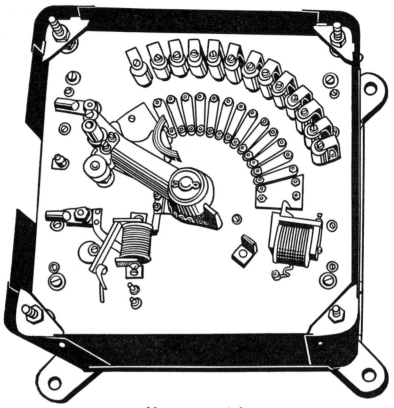

Motor starter switch

When large motors have to be started and stopped frequently the use of resistances for cutting down the current can be very wasteful, as much power is lost in them. This applies to large electric cranes and to electric trains. A subway train may have to start and stop forty or so times in the hour. In such cases the controllers are specially designed and become very complicated. In the motorman's cab is a drum-type switch, the handle of which is familiar to all of us. As the motorman turns this handle, notch by notch, to start the train, he connects various blocks of resistance to the motors, which are in series to start with, to reduce the voltage applied to each to a half. Finally the motors are connected in parallel.

The resistance in this case consists of heavy grids carried in cages under the train. If you stand by the track you can see them quite easily. Many hundreds of lives are dependent on the motorman of an electric train, so special arrangements are made in case he is suddenly taken ill. One of these devices is called a *dead-man's switch*. Should the motorman faint or die while the train is running, as his hand falls off the controller the switch is released and this switches off the current and applies the brakes.

Since most electrical equipment is stationary, the current is supplied through conductors connected to its terminals. This is impossible with a moving object like a train or bus, and various systems are in use to keep the motors supplied. Large currents are required—up to several thousands of amperes—and the two principal systems are the overhead trolley wire and the conductor rail, or third rail. In the former system the vehicle carries a flexible arm which makes a sliding or rolling contact with the wire. For small currents this may be a simple *trolley* arm with a grooved pulley on the upper end; but for heavy currents, and where the vehicle must travel in either direction without reversing the trolley arm, the *pantograph* collector is the usual type.

The pantograph is raised and lowered by air pressure and requires that the trolley wire be at a uniform level. It would never do for the overhead wire in a high-speed railway to sag between supports. That is why you have seen the rather complicated supporting wires called *catenaries*. These rise and fall along the route, being high at the supporting posts and low in the center of the span. By means of drop wires of varying lengths between the catenary and the actual conducting wire, the latter is kept horizontal. The pantograph collector thus travels along the straight wire, making continuous contact without jerks or disconnections even at high speed.

In the second method of supplying the current to trains, used particularly in cities and for limited distances, a conductor rail of special steel with a resistance only about seven or eight times that of copper is employed. This rail is carried on pedestal-type porcelain insulators fixed to the ties alongside the running rails. *Shoe collectors* fixed to the trains rub along the surface of the conductor rail and take the current to the motors. With a long electric passenger train not hauled by locomotive, the main current for the motors does not go to the motorman's cab but is picked up separately by each coach and passed straight through resistances to the motors on that coach. The motorman operates the train by remote control. When he turns his starting handle, he really sends small currents to the actual starters on the cars that have motors (some cars do not have motors). These starters control the main current. When traveling on the subway, in a motor car quite a distance away from the motorman's cab, you can distinctly hear the clang of the starter switches in that car as they are put into action one by one by the currents sent through from the motorman at the front of the train.

In practically every one of the many circuits we have described in this chapter it is necessary to introduce some device to prevent excessive current from being drawn from the source of supply. The usual method, except in very heavy currents, is to insert in the circuit a short length of conductor composed of a fusible metal and of such dimensions that it will melt and introduce a break in the circuit before damage can be caused elsewhere. In the early days such fuses consisted of a very simple arrangement with the bare fuse wire connected to two terminals. Later the wire was carried on a porcelain holder with special clips by which it could be inserted or withdrawn safely, conveniently, and quickly from fixed clips connected to the circuit.

Many of this type of fuse are still in use on low-power supplies, but modern practice aims more and more at the completely enclosed, or cartridge, fuse.

A very simple illustration of the cartridge fuse is to be found in the fuse box at home. A hard paper tube about one inch long has rounded metal ends and a single wire connecting the ends inside the tube. For heavier duty, stout porcelain barrels are used, provided with a powder filling of quartz or other fire-resisting material in which a number of wires connecting the end caps in parallel are embedded.

By paying attention to detail in the design of high-duty cartridge fuses it is possible now to hold back enormous powers with quite a small fuse, and this type has the advantage that when a fuse is blown it can be removed and replaced in a very few minutes. For heavy-current circuits, automatic circuit breakers already referred to are employed with an electromagnetic device to trip them out at a predetermined current. Some of these are so designed that even an enormous short circuit on a line, so long as it exists for a short period only, does not interrupt the supply. The breaker trips at a very high speed and then recloses again after a predetermined period, after which the trouble is probably over. This is done much more quickly than an attendant could possibly operate the switch manually.

CHAPTER 5

Electromagnetic Effects

FOR many centuries two streams of thought in the field of electricity have run side by side. In one stream men developed their ideas on electricity from the early days of amber, through galvanism and the voltaic cell, to the modern primary and secondary cells. The result is the practical circuit employed by modern electrical engineers.

The other stream led to the ship's compass and the understanding of magnetic lines of force, with a thousand and one applications. Today these streams flow together and give us electrical engineering as we know it.

The flowing together took place in Copenhagen in the year 1819, nearly twenty years after Volta had, for the first time, produced the steady electric current. Professor Hans Christian Oersted was experimenting with wires carrying a current, and it happened that he had on the table at the same time a magnetic needle pivoted to turn horizontally like a compass needle. To his astonishment he saw the needle move as he switched on the current in a nearby wire. When he introduced variations into the position of the wire he found that if it was laid parallel to the needle the current caused the needle to turn at right angles to the wire. Reversing the current resulted in the needle's turning right around and pointing in the opposite direction. Oersted

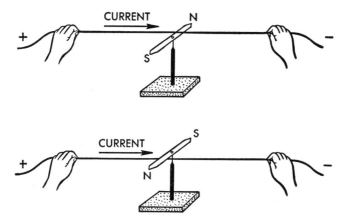

The electromagnetic effect of a current on a pivoted magnetic needle, discovered by Oersted in 1819.

also found that when the wire was below the needle the effect was in the opposite direction to what it was with the wire above the needle. Here was something new.

When this discovery was announced to the scientific world, there was great excitement. Once again a fresh mind took up the challenge of a great discovery. This time the enthusiast was a remarkable Frenchman, born at Lyons in 1775, named André Ampère, a self-taught mathematician. As a child Ampère developed a facility for mathematics, making calculations with pebbles and kidney beans. He was fascinated by figures and mastered every mathematical book he could lay his hands on. At twelve years of age he learned Latin in order to read the classical works of Euler and Bernoulli on differential calculus. Within a few years he applied himself with such steadfast purpose that he appears to have mastered the most abstruse books and worked out the problems in them.

Ampère made a great contribution to our knowledge of the electric current. He saw the importance of Oersted's discovery and invented a simple and useful rule for determining the direction of movement of the compass needle when it was deflected by the current in a wire. He imagined a little man swimming with the current in the wire while facing the needle. If the swimmer is above the needle, he swims face downward; if under the line, he swims on his back. This little *bonhomme d'Ampère,* as he was called by the professor's friends, would always find that the north pole of the magnet turned to the left.

Ampère's rule is still a very useful rule for determining the direction of current in a wire. If you are called on at any time to determine the direction of the current in a wire, bring a small compass needle near the wire and imagine yourself swimming inside the wire. If you swim with the current and face the needle, the north pole will move to your left (that is, of course, if the current is direct, not alternating).

In the course of his experiments Ampère carried Oersted's discovery much further. He found, for instance, that not only would a wire carrying a current act on a pivoted magnet but it also had an influence on another wire carrying a current. He suspended two parallel wires in such a way that they could move relatively to one another. When the current was in the same direction in both, the wires were attracted to each other. When the currents were in opposite directions, the wires repelled one another.

A simple but interesting experiment can be set up to illustrate this action. Take a coil of wire about two inches in diameter and having twenty or thirty turns. Suspend it from one end, with the lower end dipped into a small pool of mercury. Then connect a battery to the mercury and to the upper end of the coil. Immediately the coil will start to dance up and down, the lower tip of the coil sparking at the point of contact with the mercury. The action is as follows: when the lower end of the wire is touching the mercury, the current from the battery passes around the turns of the coil and each turn attracts the next one because they are parallel conductors carrying the current in the same direction. As every coil attracts the adjacent ones, the total effect is a shortening of the whole coil, and the lower end is lifted out of the mercury. This, of course, breaks the circuit, stops the current, and the turns fall back again. This restores the circuit and the current flows again; the action is thus repeated continuously. Where mercury is not available, the experiment works quite well by using a strip of light copper for the lower contact.

By following Ampère's ideas we can increase the effect of the current in a wire by passing it several times around the needle which is to be deflected through a coil of wire. In a flat coil the current in the upper wires goes one way and in the lower wires in the opposite direction. Every single wire or part of the coil has the same effect on the needle inside the coil, and the total effect is multiplied by the number of turns in the coil. The coil may, of course, take the more usual round form, but to embrace a needle of a given length this involves a greater length

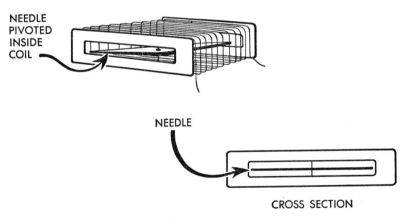

NEEDLE
PIVOTED
INSIDE
COIL

NEEDLE

CROSS SECTION

Multiplying the Oersted effect by using, instead of one wire, a number of wires made up in the form of a coil and so producing the galvanometer. The magnetic needle is pivoted inside the coil.

of wire. This idea quickly resulted in the production of an instrument for measuring current, which was called a *galvanometer*.

The simplest form of galvanometer consists of a circular coil of wire fixed in a vertical position with the magnetic needle suspended at its center. For accuracy and convenience a small magnet is used which is fitted with a long, light pointer fixed at right angles to it. The pointer moves over a horizontal scale of degrees from 0 to 90. The controlling force in such a galvanometer which keeps the needle at 0 when there is no current in the coil is the earth's magnetic field, and the stronger the current the greater the deflection against the pull of the earth's magnetism.

The action of this type of galvanometer is interesting because the reading on the scale is not proportional to the current, but the additional movement becomes less and less as the current increases. Twice the current does not give twice the movement but less than twice. The current is not proportional to the angle of the deflection but to the *tangent* of the angle. For this reason the instrument is called a *tangent* galvanometer.

Let us look at some further results of Ampère's thinking. He showed how very useful is the idea that around a wire carrying a current there is a magnetic field and magnetic lines of force. These magnetic fields can be demonstrated, like those we used in connection with permanent magnets, by the use of iron filings. The single straight wire has circular lines of force which are concentric with the wire. They extend out into space, getting weaker and weaker as the distance from the wire increases. In the case of a circular coil of wire, the lines of force enter one face of the coil, pass through the coil, and emerge from the other face.

When a coil of wire of many turns is drawn out or elongated with a hollow tube down the center, it is termed a *solenoid*. The lines of magnetic force enter at one end and leave at the other.

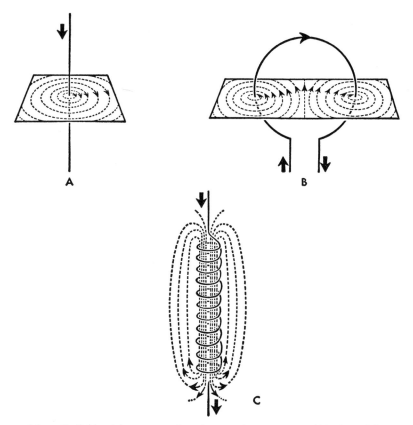

Magnetic fields of force around a wire carrying a current. (A) A straight line. (B) A circular coil. (C) A long coil, or solenoid.

A solenoid acts very much like a permanent bar magnet; that is, it has poles. The end where the lines enter the coil is the south pole and the end where they emerge is the north pole.

The similarity of the solenoid to the bar magnet can be demonstrated by making up a coil of thirty or forty turns of thin wire and fixing it to the top of a large thin cork, the underside of which is furnished with a zinc and a copper plate. The coil is connected to these plates. When the arrangement is floated on

Floating coil of wire carrying a current acts like a magnet. When free it sets itself in the direction of the earth's field. Here it is deflected by a bar magnet. The current is generated by the zinc and copper plates immersed in acid below.

weak acid, the current generated by the zinc and copper electrodes in the acid passes around the solenoid and causes it to take up a north and south position as in a ship's compass. The floating coil responds to the poles of a permanent magnet brought near in exactly the normal way. The north pole of the magnet attracts the end of the solenoid where the lines of force are entering at the south end, and repels the north end where the lines of force are emerging from the solenoid.

When a rod of soft iron is placed in a solenoid of wire carrying a current, it becomes magnetized and remains so as long as the current is flowing. Here we have the electromagnet which has so many valuable applications in modern engineering. The core attracts other pieces of iron and releases them at will by the simple switching on and off of the current. The electromagnet is used for lifting iron scrap in steelworks. When it is suspended by a crane and lowered over a pile of scrap iron which is to be moved, the odd bits and pieces stick to the core and are thus carried away. When the magnet with the crane reaches its destination, the current may be switched off and the pieces of scrap allowed to fall away without any handling whatever.

Various mechanisms in electrical engineering depend on the property of a solenoid to suck in an iron core placed near one end. In certain electric elevators the brake is normally applied by springs; but, when the motor is switched on from the cage, the current passes through a solenoid which pulls in the core against the pull of the springs and releases the brake shoes.

A well-known application of the electromagnet is the electric bell. The magnet in this case is usually of horseshoe shape. It has two limbs connected at one end by an iron bar, and each limb is provided with a coil of many turns of insulated wire. The two coils are connected in such a way that one of them sends the lines of force toward the open end of its limb and the other sends its lines of force away from the open end. The open ends are north and south, respectively, and a keeper, or armature, of soft iron placed near them is attracted. The armature in the case of the electric bell is supported from a pillar

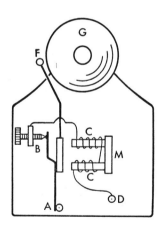

Diagram of electric bell. The current enters at terminal A, passes through the contact B, then through the coils C, of the electromagnet M, back to terminal D. When the current flows, the clapper F is pulled over to strike the gong G.

by a springy strip of metal, and can move to or from the magnet.

Connected to the armature is a metal contact which comes opposite to and touches a fixed contact carried from the base by another pillar. Two screw terminals are provided on the base and the current passes from one of them through the moving contact, then to the fixed contact, on to the coils, and back to the other terminal. The spring strip normally keeps the two contacts touching one another and the circuit is normally complete. When a battery is applied to the terminals, the magnet attracts the armature and the hammer strikes the bell. This movement breaks the circuit, the attraction ceases, and the arm springs back again. Once more the circuit is completed and so the action continues.

In bells designed for use on alternating current, as in telephone work, for instance, the moving part may be a pivoted soft iron bar "polarized" by an embracing permanent magnet. Thus the bar is attracted by current in one direction in the bell coils and repelled by current in the opposite direction. In this form of bell, no contact breaker or restoring spring is necessary.

Electric bells are made in various forms. In some of them the gong completely covers the coil and mechanism so that the hammer strikes on the inner surface of the gong. In others the mechanism is housed inside a box and there are two gongs near together on the outside of the box with the hammer projecting through the case between them, striking each in turn as it vibrates. A signaling device known as a buzzer works on a similar principle but has no gongs. In this case the spring is usually short and strong; as long as the current is connected, it emits a high-pitched buzz.

(There are many other interesting applications of the electromagnet—in telegraphy, telephones, and radio—which will be considered in detail in chapters 10 and 11.)

Wherever electric current is used, it is necessary to measure the strength of the current from time to time. This can be done by electrodeposition; but, useful as this method is for checking, it is scarcely convenient for everyday use. For practical purposes we need an instrument with a dial and a pointer from which can be read off immediately the number of amperes or milliamperes flowing in the circuit. The tangent galvanometer goes a long way in this direction but it is not portable and not direct reading; it does not give us the answer without a certain amount of preliminary calculation.

Practical ammeters are usually so constructed that the deflecting force, due to the current, is opposed by a spring. When no current is flowing, the pointer is held by the spring at the 0° on the scale. When current is flowing through the instrument, the force of the spring is overcome and the pointer moves away from 0°—the greater the current the greater the movement. The force to overcome the controlling spring is usually obtained by the interaction between a coil carrying the current to be measured and a magnetic field.

A very usual type employs a permanent magnet, horseshoe or circular in shape, with a gap between the pole pieces into which a soft-iron cylinder is inserted (see page 92). This produces two thin circular gaps across which a strong uniform magnetic field passes. The coil of wire in rectangular form is pivoted to embrace the iron cylinder and move in the gap between the cylinder and the pole pieces without touching either. When the current to be measured flows through the coil down the wires on one side—let us say on the side nearest the north pole of the magnet —they are forced in one direction around the gap. On the other side of the coil the current flows up the wires, but as they are near the south pole of the magnet the forces produce rotation in the same direction. Thus the complete coil is rotated in the gap against the force of the spring which tries to prevent its moving.

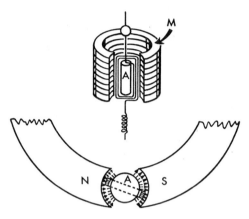

Moving-coil galvanometer. A light coil of wire is suspended in the powerful magnetic field between hollow circular pole pieces (M) and a central soft-iron core (A). The movement is indicated either by a needle pointer or by a beam of light reflected from a small mirror or to a scale.

There are two points to be remembered about moving-coil ammeters: the magnetic field of the permanent magnet is always in the same direction; and reversing the direction of flow of the current in the coil will reverse the direction of movement. Such ammeters are sometimes made with a scale having a center of 0°. The pointer not only measures the current in either one direction or the other but shows in which direction the current is flowing. With 0° at one end of the scale, usually the left-hand end, the ammeter must be correctly connected in a direct-current circuit or the pointer will not move; it will, instead, push up against the stop and try to go in the wrong direction.

Later we shall be talking about alternating currents which reverse direction sixty times a second or in radio many thousands of times a second. A moving-coil ammeter could not cope with such a situation. Half its time it would be trying to measure the current in the correct direction and the other half pushing the pointer up against the stop. This difficulty can be overcome by using a different form of ammeter called a *moving-iron* type. In this type of instrument the current to be measured is passed through the winding of an electromagnet, thus generating a magnetic field, and in this field a piece of soft iron is pivoted. No matter which way the current flows, the attraction of the iron, due to an induced polarity in the electromagnet, is the same.

The parts which carry the current in a moving-coil instrument are so light in construction that only small currents can be carried. This difficulty in measuring large currents is overcome by the use of shunts, or parallel circuits, so arranged that only a fraction of the total current to be measured passes through the instrument itself. We may have shunts of $\frac{1}{10}$, $\frac{1}{100}$, $\frac{1}{1000}$, and so on. When using a $\frac{1}{1000}$ shunt, the instrument coil carries only one ampere when the total current is 1000 amperes. The readings on the scale naturally have to be corrected for each different shunt employed. According to Ohm's law, to ensure the heavy part of the current going through the shunt, the shunt must have a lower resistance than that of the ammeter coil. A $\frac{1}{10}$ shunt on an instrument having a resistance of 90 ohms would be 10 ohms. The current in the shunt is nine times that in the

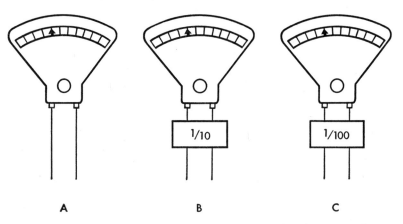

Use of instrument shunts. (A) Instrument measuring 4 amperes (no shunt). (B) Same instrument measuring 40 amps ($\frac{1}{10}$ shunt). (C) Same instrument measuring 400 amps ($\frac{1}{100}$ shunt).

instrument coil; that is, the coil carries one tenth of the whole current.

Although the measurement of current is the most important of electrical measurements, there is a need for instruments to measure voltages. Such instruments are called *voltmeters*. There are two main types of voltmeters: the electrostatic and the electromagnetic. In the electrostatic voltmeter the operation is based on the attraction between metal vanes at different potentials. A fixed system usually has a number of vanes with spaces between them, in a plane at right angles to the axis of the instrument. A similar series of vanes is carried on a suspended moving system which slides between them without touching. When there is a voltage between the fixed and moving vanes, the moving ones are sucked in between the fixed ones. As the voltage rises, the electrostatic attraction increases against the mechanical resistance of a light spring, and an attached pointer moves over a scale indicating the value of the voltage applied.

The electrostatic voltmeter is suitable for high voltages, but for ordinary voltages the electromagnetic type is the more usual. Here again, as with ammeters, there are moving-coil and moving-iron instruments. In fact, an electromagnetic voltmeter is nothing more or less than an ammeter. It is designed, however, to operate on a small current and, as Ohm's law has shown us, if the resistance of the circuit remains constant, the current will be proportional to the voltage. The instrument, though actuated by current, is deflected in proportion to the voltage applied. The scale in this case is marked not in amperes or milliamperes but in volts.

For laboratory and testing work it is often convenient to use the same instrument both as a voltmeter and as an ammeter. When used as an ammeter, it may also be used with a number of shunts for a wide range of currents. This is very conveniently done by arranging a number of resistance coils inside the instrument case connected to a set of terminals on the front or top panel. There is a separate scale for each terminal and the sequence of operations might be something like this.

Suppose we wish to test the voltage of a battery. Before connecting up any electrical equipment we must always ask ourselves, "Is it safe?" In this case we estimate the voltage of the battery and then look at the voltage scale on the instrument. We estimate it, say, as a 12-volt battery. There are two voltage scales on our instrument, one going to a maximum of 5 volts and the other to 50 volts. If we use the 5-volt terminal corresponding to the 5-volt scale, the 12-volt battery will send an excessive current through the instrument, the needle will bang hard against the upper stop, and the mechanism may be damaged. Worse, the excessive current may overheat the instrument coil and possibly burn it out. If, however, we connect the battery to the 50-volt terminal, the current through the coil is restricted by an internal resistance in the instrument and the winding is not damaged. The pointer now safely travels from 0 on the 50-volt scale and gives us a reading of 12 volts. On no account connect such a battery directly to the ammeter terminals. The shunts inside may have such a low resistance that a dangerous current would be drawn from the battery, damaging both the battery and the shunts.

Suppose the next test with such an instrument is to find how much current flows from the battery when it is connected to a number of lamps. In this case it is necessary to use the ammeter terminals. Connect one terminal of the battery to the lamps, and connect the return wire to the common terminal of the instrument; then carefully examine the ammeter terminals marked 1 ampere, 10 amperes, and so on. Try first the terminal with the largest marking. If 10 is the largest (and in trying this you find that the needle scarcely moves on the 10-ampere scale), you can turn over to the 1-ampere terminal and the deflection will be increased ten times. If the lamps are taking ½ ampere, the pointer, although giving only a tiny movement on the 10-ampere scale, will move halfway across the 1-ampere scale and you will be able to read the current accurately.

You will understand the need for this care if you imagine what would have happened if your lamps had been taking 5 amperes. On the 10-ampere terminal you would have been quite safe; the pointer would have gone halfway across and would have indicated 5 amperes. But if you had used the 1-ampere terminal to start with, the pointer would have gone clear over to the end of the scale. You might have smelled burning or have seen smoke emerging from the apparatus. Electrical measuring instruments are delicately constructed to ensure accuracy, and if you wish to maintain this accuracy you must treat them with great respect. *Always think before you connect.*

Electrical testing and measuring devices exist in many forms. They vary widely from laboratory to powerhouse, from workshop to trains, automobiles, and aircraft. There is, however, one form of ammeter which may be given special mention. It is the type of ammeter used where it is necessary to measure the current flowing through a conductor without cutting the conductor to insert an ammeter of the usual kind. The conductor may be a very large one carrying thousands of amperes, such as a bus bar in a powerhouse.

The problem of measuring a current without breaking into the circuit seems at first to be insoluble, but if we recall that around such a conductor there is a magnetic field which is proportional to the current, we see how it can be done. We measure the magnetic field and convert the reading into amperes. In the type of ammeter under discussion a split iron bar is threaded around the cable in the form of a pair of tongs; the handle carries the dial, scale, and pointer for indicating the current.

There are many situations in generating stations, in industrial plants, and in research laboratories where the value of the voltage and current in a circuit are required so frequently that it is out of the question to have men reading the type of instrument we have been talking about, and writing down the result. It would take too long and would cost too much, so instruments do the note taking. When we want an answer after many hours or possibly even days, we take the notes from the instrument and examine the results which have been recorded.

The notes are certainly of a special kind. Sometimes they are on a disk of paper and sometimes on a strip of paper many feet long and rolled on a drum, or cylinder. The disk type is slowly rotated clockwise by an electric motor, perhaps once a day, and the information is marked on it from time to time as required. In the drum type the roll of paper unwinds, is marked, and winds up again on a second roll that is driven mechanically or electrically at a constant speed.

The automatic note taking in these recording instruments is done by a pen such as is used in barographs or in recording thermometers. A light pen, fixed to the pointer of the ammeter, voltmeter, or other instrument, marks the paper as the disk turns or the drum unwinds. In the disk type the pen moves from the center to the outside of the circular chart; in the drum type it moves across the paper strip, but in both cases the movement is across the direction of travel of the paper. Thus a curve is drawn showing the continuous variation of volts, amperes, or other quantity which is to be recorded.

When the recording instrument is very delicate and not strong enough to drag the pen across the paper, an ingenious modification is used, called the thread recorder. In this type the pen is positioned close to but not touching the paper. It normally floats freely, as does the pointer on the ordinary voltmeter or ammeter near to the scale. Across the front of the instrument, however, is stretched a fine thread carried by a simple mechanism which pushes it toward the paper at intervals, carrying the pen with it. The moving pen lever is normally free to take up its correct position controlled by the voltage or current and without any mechanical restraint, but when the thread advances at intervals it pushes the pen instantaneously onto the paper, makes a dot, and retracts again. Instead of a continuous line, the ultimate record consists of a series of closely placed dots.

So far, this chapter on electromagnetic effects has dealt with the form and direction of the magnetic field around a straight wire carrying a current, and the multiplying of this effect by coiling the wire into a ring or a spiral. We have seen how a piece of iron rod is sucked into a solenoid and what happens to it when it gets there, and we have studied the important sphere of application in which the magnetic field generated by a current is used in constructing electrical measuring instruments like ammeters and voltmeters. There is another interesting application of importance, the electric motor. We have only to think of the vast field of electric power—from small motors on sewing machines, vacuum cleaners, and toy trains to the monsters which drive rolling mills in steel plants and wind up the cages in coal mines—to appreciate the importance of the electric motor.

Not very long after the electric current had been discovered by Volta in 1800 men began to see the possibility of obtaining mechanical movement and power from electric current. Much discussion took place but Michael Faraday carried out a practical experiment which, simple as it was, started the development of the electric motor.

Faraday suspended a six-inch length of wire—one-fifth of an inch thick—by a hook at one end. The lower end was dipped in a bowl of mercury. In the center of the bowl was a permanent magnet fixed vertically. He then passed a current from the hook through the wire into the mercury, and found that the wire began to rotate around the magnet and continued to rotate as long as the current flowed. On Christmas Day, 1821, he carried the experiment to a climax: the magnet was removed and the wire was spun around only by the earth's magnetic field. We read that Faraday was so delighted that he fetched his wife from her Christmas preparations and danced around exclaiming, "There they go! There they go! We have succeeded at last." He was so pleased with the result that he invited his assistant to choose a theater and they went off together "to see the horses at Astley's."

The fundamental fact is that a wire carrying a current in a magnetic field is subjected to a force pushing it sideways. This is because the wire is in a magnetic field and develops a magnetic field of its own. The resulting combination of magnetic fields is a crowding of lines of force on one side of the wire and a thinning of them on the other. The wire is forced from the crowded side to the thinned side. The diagram shows a field from left to right between two magnet poles and a wire with the current going down from you through the diagram. The field due to the current strengthens the field due to the magnet above the wire and weakens it below. The wire is forced down.

There is a useful rule for determining the direction that a wire

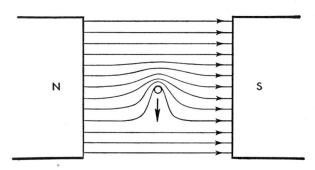

Disturbance of magnetic field by current in a wire creates a force tending to move the wire at right angles to the field; with current flowing in the conductor down through the paper, the conductor is forced in the direction of the arrow.

will move in a magnetic field. It is called the left-hand rule. Hold your left hand with the thumb, first and second fingers at right angles to one another. Point the first finger in the direction of the magnetic field and the second in the direction of the current in the wire. The movement of the wire will be in the direction the thumb is pointing.

*F*irst finger	lines of *F*orce
se*C*ond finger	*C*urrent
thu*M*b	*M*otion

Now look at the diagram, hold your left hand over it with the two fingers and thumb extended and you can check the left-hand rule as follows:

first finger	pointing to the right
second finger	through the page
thumb	down the page

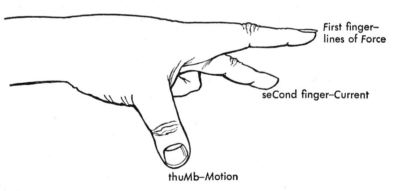

First finger–
lines of Force

seCond finger–Current

thuMb–Motion

Left-hand rule for use with electric motor or any current-carrying conductor in a magnetic field.

And what happens to a wire in the same field but with the current coming up through the page? Try the left-hand rule and see for yourself.

Now suppose we make a square coil of two wires in the magnetic field and fix the coil to a central spindle so that, instead of moving up and down, they rotate. We connect the wires at the far end and lead current in and out at the near end. Fortunately for our experiment one wire goes down and the other goes up, so they can be connected to the same spindle. The whole coil and its spindle begin to rotate in a clockwise direction. Wire *A* goes up and wire *B* goes down. (See illustration on page 102.)

When the coil reaches a vertical position there is no longer any magnetic force to make it rotate. The two wires are now pulling in opposite directions. Suppose, however, we reverse the current and give the coil the merest push beyond the mid-position. Wire *A* with its current reversed goes down and wire *B* goes up. The coil continues to rotate in a clockwise direction.

All we need to do to make a continuously running motor out of our simple coil and magnet is to fit a device which will reverse the current in the coil every time it gets into the vertical position across the magnetic field. This device is called a *commutator*. It consists of a metal cylinder, usually of copper, split into two halves which are separately insulated from the spindle. The two ends of the coil are solidly connected to the two halves, or segments, of the commutator; and the current is led in and out by metallic brushes which are fixed to the base of the motor and rub against the segments on opposite sides. You will see that the coil consisting of conductors *A* and *B* has current in one direction for half a revolution and in the opposite direction for the next half, quite automatically. As it spins around, its momentum carries it over the "dead" position each half revolution, and it goes on spinning as long as the current is applied.

Over the years this very rudimentary idea for a motor has passed through many stages of development. Instead of one coil consisting of two wires, a "go" and a "return," many turns of wire are used in the coil to increase the effect. The pole pieces are

not flat as shown in the diagram on page 99 but curved to fit the
path of the spinning coil. The coils, instead of being self-support-

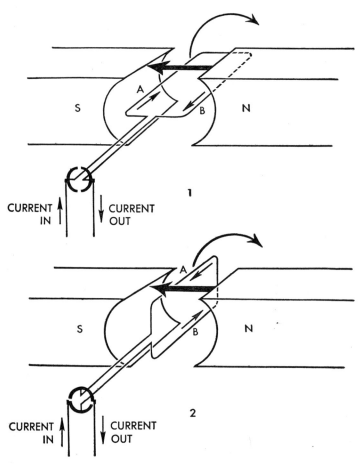

*How a simple electric motor works. A flat coil of wire has its two ends
connected to the two halves of a commutator. Heavy arrow shows direction of magnetic force. As the coil and the commutator rotate in the
magnetic field, the current in the coil entering and leaving by the brushes
is reversed twice every revolution. In conductor A the current first flows
from front to back and in conductor B from back to front. Both produce
a clockwise rotation. (1) Coil in position of maximum effect. (2) One-
quarter revolution later: commutator reversing connections.*

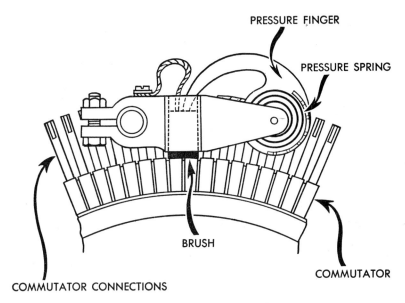

PRESSURE FINGER

PRESSURE SPRING

BRUSH

COMMUTATOR

COMMUTATOR CONNECTIONS

DC motor commutator and brush gear.

ing in air, are wound in slots on an iron armature almost filling the space between the pole pieces. This increases the strength of the magnetic field.

Then again, instead of one coil with many turns of wire, many coils are distributed around the armature and this results in a smoother movement. The commutator, instead of having two segments, has a large number according to the number of coils in the armature. The reversal of current now takes place many times during the revolution instead of only twice.

The electric motor, one of the most workable of mechanical devices, reaches over 90 per cent efficiency. To achieve this result, great care is taken in armature construction. The magnetic field through the rotating armature is being continuously reversed hundreds of times a minute as it spins around; and, as you will see from the later explanation of the dynamo, there is a natural tendency for eddy currents to be generated in the iron.

This and the resulting heating are avoided by building the armature of thin sheet-steel stampings, or laminations, about a fiftieth of an inch thick. These are pressed together hydraulically after being coated individually with insulating compound. Sometimes the laminations are coated with thin paper before being assembled.

The construction of the practical commutator with its many segments is a work of art. All the segments have to be insulated from one another and this is usually done with thin sheets of mica, a pale brown or reddish semitransparent flaky mineral substance. The high insulating properties of mica make it capable of withstanding heat. After assembly and clamping together with end rings, the outer surface is turned and polished in a lathe. The brushes for leading the current in and out by rubbing on this surface are usually made of carbon and are carried in metal holders with springs to keep them in contact with the rotating commutator.

In large motors many hundreds of amperes have to be led in and out of the armatures. It is essential therefore to maintain a good rubbing contact between the brush and the commutator to prevent sparking. Even in the small motors used in vacuum cleaners, any irregularities or dirt will cause sparking and ultimate breakdown.

The method adopted for creating the magnetic field in the electric motor is very important. Permanent magnets are not used, but, rather, a field magnet which consists of an iron or steel core on which is wound a large number of turns of wire carrying a current. The usual form is a heavy ring with the pole pieces turned inward toward the central armature. The number of pairs of poles varies with the particular use. There can be many more than in the simple motor but of course there is always an even number, as many north poles as south. The majority of motors today have four poles on the field magnet, though large machines like rolling mill motors have up to twenty poles. This is useful for the slow speeds required.

The application of the electric motor has had a great influence on the layout of manufacturing plants. Years ago a whole mill would be driven by one large reciprocating steam engine and the power transmitted to the machines by shafting and flying belts. Today every machine has its own individual motor drive with its own separate controlling device; this makes for both efficiency and safety. The long lines of steel shafting and noisy leather belts on pulleys have gone, and the power reaches the machine silently and unobtrusively through hidden electric cables. This is a remarkable development from Faraday's simple spinning wire. The next chapter will show how this great man made even more important discoveries.

CHAPTER 6

Mechanical Generation
of Electricity

MICHAEL FARADAY had a profound influence on scientific discovery. In electricity his contributions were fundamental, almost miraculous, and he also made great advances in chemistry: liquefying gases, alloying steel, making glass for optical purposes, to name but a few.

From his boyhood throughout his life Faraday displayed a high standard of integrity, an indefatigable energy, and a clarity of mind which led him step by step to his great discoveries. In all respects his was a charming personality with an intuition which brought him scientific results, and a modest friendliness which made individuals and audiences love him.

Dates are sometimes irksome but not in this case. In the year 1800 Volta announced the steady continuous electric current. Michael Faraday was born in 1791; so, while Volta was puzzling over Galvani's twitching frogs' legs in Italy and making his voltaic cell, the great Faraday, who was to build a wonderful edifice of scientific development on Volta's discovery, was a lad of nine running about the streets of London. He had no thought then that before he died in 1867 he would have declined the presidency of the Royal Society, lectured before the highest in the

106

land, advised governments, and, after more than half a century of inspired experiments, made the Royal Institution in London the very birthplace and first home of modern electrical science.

Faraday's father was a blacksmith and the family had rooms over a coachhouse in a mews near Manchester Square. But Michael Faraday's boyhood came to an end earlier than most boys. His parents were so poor that at the age of ten he began work at a bookseller's in Blandford Street, near his home. On Mondays his mother gave him a loaf of bread to manage for himself; he marked it into fourteen portions for the week's morning and evening meals.

Within a few years he was apprenticed as a bookbinder, a fortunate occurrence, for the many scientific books which passed through his hands absorbed his attention and he kept a notebook in which he entered items of special interest. By the age of twenty-one Faraday had informed himself thoroughly on the known facts about general science and in particular the progress of electricity; on occasions he surprised distinguished visitors to the workshop with his grasp of the subject. In his spare time during this period he made experimental apparatus and his electrical machine is preserved to this day in the museum of the Royal Institution.

About this time Faraday wrote an interesting letter to a friend:

> I, Sir, I my own self, cut out seven discs of the size of half-pennies each! I, Sir, covered them with seven half-pence, and I interposed between seven, or rather six, pieces of paper soaked in a solution of muriate of soda! But laugh no longer, dear A.; rather wonder at the effects this trivial power produced. It was sufficient to produce the decomposition of sulphate of magnesia —an effect which extremely surprised me; for I did not, could not, have any idea that the agent was competent to the purpose.

What a remarkable prediction of things to come! And how quickly they came, too, for in the spring of 1812 Sir Humphry

Davy was giving a course of four lectures on chemistry at the Royal Institution and a customer gave Michael a ticket for the lectures. With great excitement the poor bookbinding apprentice took his seat in the gallery (a guide will show you the place to-day, over the clock) and eagerly wrote notes on the lectures. At the end of the course he wrote up the notes, bound them attractively, and sent them to the lecturer with a request that he should be appointed as assistant in the laboratory. These notes, too, are a treasured possession of the Royal Institution not only because of their subject matter but because they reveal the courage and at the same time the character of Faraday. In one place in these notes he wrote:

> Mr. Davy now noticed the proportions in which chlorine, oxygen and hydrogen unite to each other and advanced it as an instance of the truth of definite proportions. Here he gave the proportions in numbers comparing the specific gravity and the volume together. But his delivery at this moment being particularly quick and the proportions and comparisons being expressed rapidly one after the other, I was unable to take them accurately down, therefore lest I should err in my statement I have left this part of the lecture out; should I by any lucky opportunity gain it, I will insert it below.

The blank was never filled but remains to this day to remind us of the character of this great man. Never throughout a long career as a scientific observer did he record as fact what he had not confirmed by every possible means in his power.

The notes were made in the spring and sent to Davy in the fall, and it is worth while recalling that during these months history was being made elsewhere. While the foundation of our electrical heritage was being quietly laid in the mind of the un-noticed Faraday, the eyes of the world were on a great drama in Europe. Between the taking of the notes in April and the sending of the bound volume to Davy in December an army of 600,-000 men had marched triumphantly across Russia, had captured

Moscow, and had then been overtaken by one of the greatest tragedies in military history. Faraday does not rest in such a famous place as Les Invalides, but in a modest tomb in Highgate Cemetery, yet his influence on world progress is infinitely greater than that of his contemporary, Napoleon.

Sir Humphry Davy found Faraday's application for employment rather a problem. Here was a youth of outstanding ability but there was no vacancy. Davy immediately asked the advice of a Mr. Pepys (not the diarist), one of the institution's governors, who replied, "Let him wash bottles. If he is any good he will accept the work, if he refuses he is not good for anything."

And we read that one night the Faraday family was just going to bed when there was a loud knock on the door and, looking out, they saw a grand carriage and a footman with a message. It was from Sir Humphry Davy requesting Faraday to call and see him the next morning at the Royal Institution.

There was a vacancy and, at the age of twenty-one, Michael Faraday was appointed assistant at twenty-five shillings a week. So started that remarkable career lasting for nearly half a century, during which he became a skillful experimenter and a fluent and enthusiastic lecturer, so much so that the "Friday evening discourses," which he originated, have remained a popular and widely famous feature of the Royal Institution and of London life.

In 1819 Oersted, the Danish professor, had shown that electricity produced magnetism. This set many minds pondering the connection. If electricity could produce magnetism, then why could not magnetism produce electricity?

Five years later a French scientist named Arago carried out an experiment which brought the problem right out into the daylight. He observed various phenomena when a sheet of metal was held near a moving magnet. He crystallized his observations in one famous experiment known as Arago's disk. He constructed a piece of apparatus with a pivoted disk of copper which could be rotated rapidly about a vertical axis. The disk was made to rotate by a hand wheel and cord passing around a small pulley on the spindle which carried the disk. Through the center of the spindle, made hollow for the purpose, he placed a steel pivot with a pointed upper end on which a large magnetic needle was balanced. There was no mechanical connection between the rotating disk and the needle that floated just above it; and, to ensure that no currents of air should be set up by the disk to influence the needle, a sheet of glass was inserted between the disk and the needle, the sheet having a small hole to permit the passage of the pivot.

Arago found that, when the handle was turned and the disk rotated, the needle followed in the same direction. When the direction of rotation of the disk was reversed, the needle moved in the opposite direction. It was as if there were invisible cords connecting the needle to the disk, dragging it around. When the magnetic needle was replaced by a bar of soft iron, the effect disappeared; neither was there any movement with wood or brass bars, only with a magnet.

We now know that the source of attraction between the cop-

Arago's disk. The compass needle, suspended above a glass sheet, is dragged around by the eddy currents induced in the rotating copper disk.

per disk and the magnet lay in the eddy currents which were induced in the disk as it moved past the magnet. These were set up by the magnetic field moving across the disk and, once they were flowing, they interacted on the magnet, pulling it after them.

Whenever a magnetic field is made to move through a conductor, eddy currents are set up in it. If we have a powerful magnet and drop a coin between the poles, we find that there is a certain reluctance on the part of the coin to pass through the gap; it slows down or tends to move sideways out of the gap due to the reaction between the eddy currents induced in the coin and the magnetic field. If we force the coin in and out of the field rapidly, we find further that it becomes warm because of the eddy currents flowing in it.

This principle is ingeniously employed today in automatic vending machines. The coin we insert is scrutinized very carefully by the machine before it hands over the candy bar. After being gauged for diameter and thickness by passing through a slot, the coin falls through a magnetic field. If it is made of the correct metal the eddy currents induced in it deflect it sideways. This is sufficient to make the coin hit a metal anvil from which it bounces, if of correct weight, through a slot to operate the mechanism. If the coin fails in any of these tests, even if its eddy currents are wrong, it is rejected. The whole process takes just five seconds.

Faraday's studies led him to give much thought to this experiment of Arago's and in his diary we read:

> It appeared very extraordinary, that as every electric current was accompanied by a corresponding intensity of magnetic action at right angles to the current, good conductors of electricity, when placed within the sphere of its action, should not have any current induced in them. These considerations, with their consequence, the hope of obtaining electricity from ordinary magnetism, have stimulated me at various times to investigate experimentally the inductive effects of electric currents. I

lately arrived at positive results; and not only had my hopes fulfilled, but obtained a key which appeared to me to open out a full explanation of Arago's magnetic phenomena.

The year was 1831. Faraday had tried many combinations of magnet and coil to see if he could generate an electric current from magnetism. In August of that year he made a most important discovery which will be discussed in the next chapter on the transformer, but in October he did something even more remarkable. He thrust a permanent bar magnet into a solenoid (a hollow coil of wire), the ends of which were connected to a galvanometer. Immediately there was a deflection and he found that he had generated electricity from magnetism. When the magnet was fully inserted, the current ceased; but, as he withdrew it, again a current flowed, this time in the opposite direction. The current flowed only while the magnet was in motion. This was the beginning of electromagnetic induction, which is the basis of the dynamo and the alternator, the very first demonstration of the mechanical generation of electricity.

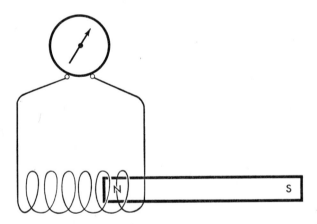

The first mechanical generation of an electric current: Faraday's experiment with magnet and coil connected to a galvanometer. Inserting the magnet into the coil generates a current in one direction. Withdrawing it generates a current in the opposite direction.

Faraday was disappointed at the transient nature of the current; he was looking for something like the current given by the voltaic pile, one which continued as long as the circuit was complete. But he would not leave it there. When he saw the magnetic needle in the experiment with Arago's disk continuously chasing the rotating disk, he knew that the induction was continuous and not intermittent. He accordingly procured a powerful permanent magnet and mounted a disk of copper so that it could be rotated through the gap between the poles. He then connected a pair of sliding contacts, one on the axle and the other on the rim of the disk, to a galvanometer and made the next remarkable discovery: the galvanometer was deflected continuously so long as the disk remained turning.

The results which Faraday obtained during these few important weeks were written up in his *Experimental Researches, First Series*. So much resulted from the discoveries explained in them that these notes make interesting reading. In his sharing of his boylike pleasure and enthusiasm over the success of his experiments, we see exactly how, from the brain of this great but modest man, came the whole field of electrical supply from power-driven generators.

In a practical machine, rotation of the parts is usually essential. Pushing and pulling a magnet in and out of a solenoid is altogether unmechanical; and even the rotating disk, while securing continuous rotary motion, was very inefficient. The current collected by the sliding contacts was only a fraction of that generated; the rest circulated internally within the disk as eddy current and was for all practical purposes completely lost. It was soon found that, instead of the copper disk, a coil of wire could be rotated between the poles of the magnet and the whole of the current generated led out for useful work.

In principle, then, an electric generator consists simply of two parts: (1) a magnetic field, and (2) a rotating coil of wire. In

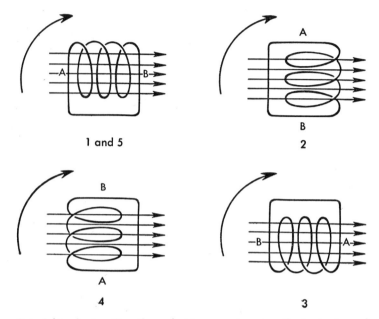

1 and 5

2

4

3

Principles of operation of an electric generator. A coil of wire is made to rotate in a magnetic field. (1) Coil receives field through face A. (2) No field threads through coil. (3) Coil receives field through face B. (4) No field threads through coil. (5) Condition 1 restored.

one position the coil receives the lines of force from, say, side *A*. After a quarter revolution it receives no lines of force because it lies along the direction of the magnetic field. After half a revolution it has turned side for side and the lines of force pass through the coil but in the direction opposite to the original position. Three-quarters of the way around (position 4) there are again no lines of force threading the coil; and, after a complete revolution (position 5), the original conditions are restored.

A comparison of Faraday's coil and magnet experiment with the conditions in the rotating coil shows that they are identical. Lines of force are thrust from one side of the coil and the motion dies away; the field is then thrust into the coil in the opposite direction and again the motion dies away. This sequence of events is known as a cycle and is very important in electrical engineering, particularly when we come to alternating currents and talk of so many cycles per second. This action of the rotating coil in a magnetic field is a most fundamental and important idea.

It is all very well to talk of a simple coil in a simple magnetic field, but in a real dynamo we have to introduce several important practical features. As with the electric motor already described, the coil in a simple form of dynamo is wound with many turns on an iron armature which rotates between the curved poles of the field magnet. The two ends of the coil are brought to the segments of a commutator where sliding brushes carry the current away for use.

With the motor, we discovered a useful rule for determining which way the coil would move under the electromagnetic force. In the same way there is a useful rule for determining the direction of the current induced in a coil moving in a magnet. This is known as the right-hand rule. Again:

thu*M*b	direction of *M*otion.
*F*irst finger	lines of *F*orce.
s*E*cond finger	direction of the *E*lectromotive force which pushes the current along the wire.

It is interesting to note at this stage that a dynamo is really an alternator. If the two ends of the coil were connected to two insulated slip rings on the spindle, the current delivered to the brushes would reverse once every revolution. It is only by the use of the commutator that the alternating current generated in the rotating coil is converted into a direct current.

There is really no fundamental difference between a motor and a dynamo. If we construct a dynamo as indicated in this chapter and then connect a sufficiently powerful battery, it will rotate and do work exactly as described in chapter 5. Understanding the principle of the dynamo now, however, we can fill a gap in our motor knowledge.

When a motor is rotated by a current, it cannot avoid being a dynamo; at the same time it has all the necessary parts: coil, magnetic field, commutator. As it spins in the direction given in the left-hand rule, it tries to generate a current in the direction given by the right-hand rule.

Put up your two hands with the two thumbs pointing in the same direction, say to the left, with the back of the right hand and the palm of the left hand facing you. The left hand represents the action of the conductor as a motor moving to the left, the right hand the same conductor as a dynamo. Suppose the lines of magnetic force are traveling upward. Both your first fingers are up, indicating this direction. Now look at your second fingers. The left-hand second finger is pointing toward you and that is the current driving the motor; but the right-hand second finger is pointing away from you, in the opposite direction.

Your right hand, expressing the dynamo rule, tells you the conductor traveling through the magnetic field is generating an *emf* (electromotive force) or voltage, whichever you prefer, in a direction opposite to the flow of the current entering the motor from outside. This is called the *back emf*. Suppose such a motor is stationary and you switch it on but prevent it from turning by holding it in some way against the turning force. Now the conductors are not moving in the magnetic field; the machine is not acting as a dynamo and there is no back emf. There is, therefore, a rush of current which may be so great in a large motor as to be dangerous and that is why carefully designed motor starters have to be used. These starters control the current by adding outside resistance until the motor has gained speed and so produced the back emf, which then takes charge and opposes the incoming current.

The back emf makes an electric motor adjust itself to the load. When an electric train is running on the level, it takes a certain current from the trolley wire or third rail because of the difference between the main's voltage and the back emf at that speed. When it comes to an incline, the motor naturally slows down and, as a dynamo, immediately generates less back emf. Thus more current can flow in from the mains to keep the train going.

Similarly, when the train comes to a decline, it accelerates and the back emf increases, stopping the unwanted current. In the same way a motor driving a piece of machinery adjusts itself in this convenient manner. You will notice in a workshop where the current feeding a motor on a bench saw is indicated by an ammeter that the ammeter reading is quite small while the saw is idling. As soon as a piece of wood is brought up to it and cutting starts, the current increases and remains high until the length of wood is cut through, when it drops again. Back emf is a most useful and important feature, and accounts for the remarkable versatility of the electric motor.

Now let us get back to the electric generator. The permanent magnet to create the magnetic field was soon superseded by the electromagnet, and in the early days separate machines known as *exciters* were used to generate the current to supply the field magnets of the main machine. The exciters themselves depended for their magnetic field on permanent magnets and were often mounted on the top of the main machine. It was soon discovered that the current from the dynamo itself could be used for exciting the field magnet. There was enough permanent magnetism in the core to start up a small voltage in the armature when it was rotated, and this in turn strengthened the field, giving still more voltage and, in due course, the full output was attained.

Direct current is required in the field coils because the mag-

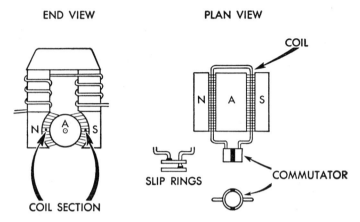

 END VIEW   PLAN VIEW

Principle of dynamo, showing magnetic field generated by an electromagnet. (A) Armature. (N, S) Poles. Using slip rings gives an alternating current. To get direct current, the commutator is necessary.

netic field must always be in the same direction. To obtain this direct current in alternators where the current is not taken off through a commutator, a separate exciter is still necessary. Today this special machine is mounted on the end of the main spindle.

So long as there is relative motion between the magnetic field and the coils in which the current is to be generated, it is immaterial which one rotates. The field magnet with its magnetic field may be stationary, constituting the frame of the machine as in the usual form of dynamo, or the coils may be stationary and the field made to rotate.

In practical alternators for generating electric power, rotating field magnets and stationary armatures are in common use. The rotating system of field magnets is called the *rotor* and the outside frame with its coils is called the *stator*. There is one great advantage in this arrangement. The large currents which are generated do not have to pass through slip rings and brushes as they would have to do if the coil rotated. Since they are stationary, the current from them can be led out through permanent fixed connections. As the field magnets rotate, current to generate the field must be supplied through slip rings, but this is a much simpler matter as low-voltage direct current is sufficient for the purpose. The current taken from the stationary generating coils is alternating and may be of high voltage, up to 30,000 volts.

When alternators are driven by steam turbines or by diesel engines, the spindle is usually horizontal, but in water power stations the turbine is often below the engine room floor down in the concrete foundations and a vertical spindle comes up to the generator on the level of the powerhouse. In this case the generator stands, as it were, on its end.

Another important distinction between one type of alternator and another is the speed of the prime mover, whether engine or turbine. When a relatively low-speed water turbine or diesel engine is used, there must be many poles on the rotating magnet. A high-speed turbine needs only a few. This is easily understood.

Suppose an alternator gives current at a frequency of 60 cycles a second and is driven by a steam turbine at 3,600 revolutions a minute, or 60 revolutions a second. One pair of poles on the rotating magnet is sufficient because the magnetic field from the two poles, a north and a south pole, sweeps past the winding 60 times every second and induces a current with a frequency of 60 cycles a second. With a slower speed of, say, 600 revolutions a minute, it is necessary to have twelve poles on the rotating magnet. Six hundred revolutions per minute, or 10 per second, means six pairs of poles for a 60-cycle current.

Let us look at some typical generators in detail. First, take a steam-driven set in which the alternator is driven by a steam turbine. When you see one of these machines in a modern powerhouse, you will be impressed by its size. It is so long that it is jokingly said that in designing them allowance must be made for the curvature of the earth! About half the length is occupied by the steam turbine, which can be distinguished by the

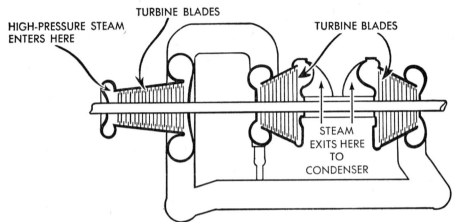

Section of a large steam-turbo alternator. The steam end.

enormous steam pipes connecting one part with another. The central spindle of the turbine continues on through the main generator, a large cylindrical box, and then on to the exciter and possibly other auxiliary machines at the end.

Our interest lies in the inside of the large cylindrical box. A sheet-steel casing encloses the details, but if we were to be present when the casing is removed for inspection or, better still, if we could inspect the machine during manufacture we could see the stator. This is a massive steel construction with a tunnel along its center and at each end a complex of insulated conductors.

To create the voltage for the fundamental generator we must sweep a conductor through a magnetic field, or, alternatively, sweep a magnetic field past a conductor. In the type of generator we are examining, we do the latter. We generate a powerful magnetic field in the rotor which fits closely and rotates in the tunnel within the stator. This field is swept past the conductors housed in longitudinal slots along the tunnel of the stator (see the illustration above). The sloping conductors at the end are simply the connections from the active conductors in the slots;

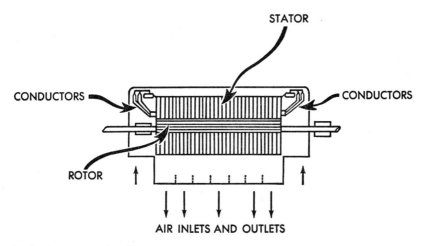

STATOR

CONDUCTORS

CONDUCTORS

ROTOR

AIR INLETS AND OUTLETS

Turboalternator. The alternator end.

they connect the individual straight conductors in proper order with the main strips that lead to the transformers.

With the number of conductors inside an alternator stator, a good deal of heat is generated by the flow of current. In a large machine it may be the equivalent of one hundred domestic electric space heaters. If this heat were not dissipated, dangerous temperature rises would result during operation. To prevent this from happening, air ducts are provided throughout the structure.

Even such an apparently simple matter as air cooling has given the electrical designer an opportunity for ingenuity, and he has discovered that the gas hydrogen has many advantages over air for the purpose. Hydrogen carries the heat away better than air; it does not cause so much drag on the high-speed rotating rotor; and it prevents certain other bad effects which accompany the use of air for the purpose. All large modern turbo alternators are cooled with hydrogen. Very great care is taken, of course, to keep the cooling hydrogen pure and to avoid leakage into the machine.

Now the complete stator is ready for the rotor. All that is required magnetically is a two-pole magnet, but the practical achievement of this requirement introduces a variety of refinements. When completed, the rotor has the simple appearance of a long smooth cylinder reduced in diameter at both ends for the supporting bearings in which it revolves. It is slightly smaller than the tunnel in the stator, for it must not touch the walls of the tunnel. A rotor for a large modern generator may be over twenty-five feet long, about three feet in diameter, and weigh over twenty-five tons.

Although only two magnetic poles are required, the windings for the exciting current are again housed in slots in the surface of the steel cylinder. The effect is something like that diagramed here. Because of the high speed—60 revolutions a second—the steel and the wire in the slots are subject to enormous forces. Each pound of material experiences a force of several pounds, which

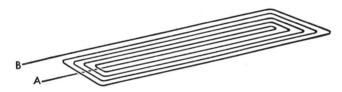

FLAT COIL

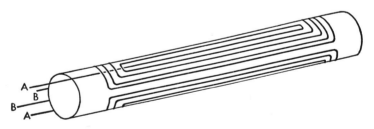

SHAPE OF COIL WHEN APPLIED
TO STEEL CORE

Two-pole rotor winding.

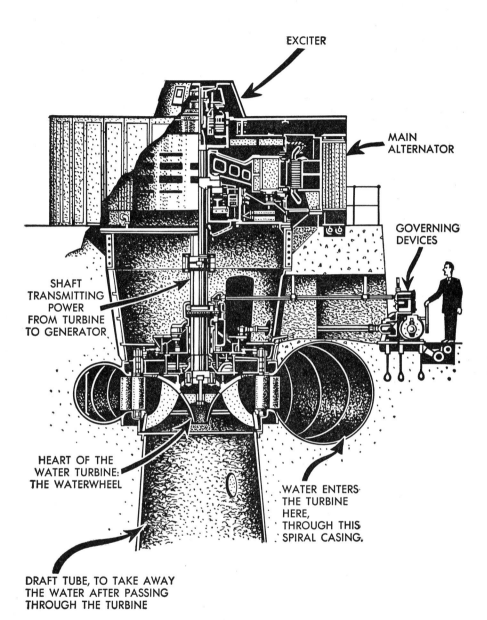

EXCITER

MAIN
ALTERNATOR

GOVERNING
DEVICES

SHAFT
TRANSMITTING
POWER
FROM TURBINE
TO GENERATOR

HEART OF THE
WATER TURBINE:
THE WATERWHEEL

WATER ENTERS
THE TURBINE
HERE,
THROUGH THIS
SPIRAL CASING.

DRAFT TUBE, TO TAKE AWAY
THE WATER AFTER PASSING
THROUGH THE TURBINE

*Section of a large hydroelectric generator. (Adapted from The English
Electric Co. Ltd.)*

tends to wrench it apart, and the whole rotor is subject to a bursting force of 20,000 tons or more.

To give the conductors every help in such an arduous situation it is usual to insulate them with glass, mica tape, or asbestos and to secure them in the slots with wedges of a nonmagnetic metal such as phosphor bronze. The smooth appearance at the ends is also accounted for by the fact that the end turns of a conductor are enclosed in supporting nonmagnetic metal shields.

The construction and appearance of generators which are driven by water power are very different from those of the steam-turbo alternator just described. The two main types—those with horizontal spindles like the steam turbine and the vertical-spindle type—are designed for the particular *head,* or pressure, of water available. High-speed machines usually have horizontal shafts and low-speed have vertical shafts. The appearance of a large hydroelectric station is very different from that of a steam station. All that we see of the sets in the powerhouse are the round covered-in generators, as shown on page 123. The large diameter of these is due to the dimensions of the many-pole rotor and the turbines are down below the floor out of sight.

CHAPTER 7

AC and the Transformer

I N the early days of electrical development direct current (DC) was looked upon as the natural kind of current. It was the kind produced by batteries and was the kind that led to the many applications in electrochemistry—decomposition of complex substances, plating of metals, and so on. It was also the kind of current that produced magnetic effects when passed through coils of wire, opening up a wide field of application.

When mechanical generation of electricity came in and the dynamo began to supersede the battery, it is not surprising that DC should have been taken for granted. When it was found that the current produced by rotating a coil of wire in a magnetic field reversed its direction twice every revolution, this was felt to be a nuisance. So, to produce the proper sort of current, the commutator was invented and the current leaving the machine was made to travel continuously around the circuit in one direction.

There are still many uses for DC, but the field of application of alternating current (AC) has become much more important. Power stations generate AC. The current transmitted across the country and distributed for industrial and domestic use is AC; and, where DC systems still survive in some of our towns, every effort is being made to convert them to AC. For special requirements—such as electric railways, charging batteries, electrolytic refining of metals, and so on—AC is not suitable. For these cases AC is generated and is then converted, or rectified, into DC for use. In the extensive fields of telephony, radio, and television, AC is essential: many of the results obtained depend entirely on the way in which AC works and could not possibly be obtained with DC. So AC becomes a subject in itself; it opens up a new electrical world.

Alternating current flows in one direction for a period of time and then in the opposite direction for an equal period. It then starts again in the original direction and continues the sequence. We call the complete time taken to flow one way and then the other a *cycle* and there are so many cycles a second. The public electricity supply is provided at 60 cycles per second (50 in England and some other countries). This means that in $\frac{1}{60}$ second the current starts from nothing, rises to a maximum, falls to nothing, starts off again in the opposite direction, rises to a maximum and again falls to nothing.

When we look at the bright filament of an electric bulb we know that 120 times every second there is no current whatever flowing in it. This happens every time the current is reversed. The illusion of continuous brilliance is due to two factors. In the first place persistence of vision prevents the eye from following changes beyond a certain speed and, secondly, the filament cannot cool rapidly enough to follow the changes of current. When there were supply systems working on lower frequencies —for example, 25 cycles per second—the fluctuations were quite noticeable to the eye.

In discussing alternating currents, electrical engineers often speak of the *sine* curve. This is the curve that shows how AC varies with time. The current does not jump from nothing instantly to a maximum and then after a short period jump back again; it travels smoothly and without jerks as the curve in-

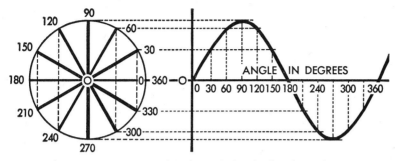

How the sine curve representing the variation in the alternating current over a single cycle originates from the circular motion of the generator.

dicates. Above the line represents current in one direction, the positive direction, and below the line represents current in the opposite, or negative, direction.

The intermittent nature of alternating current can be demonstrated by a very simple experiment. If we swing a white stick rapidly against a dark background in a room illuminated by electric bulbs supplied by AC, the stick will not have a blurred appearance but will show a number of distinct, separate, or phantom sticks. It is quite easy in this way to calculate roughly the frequency of AC. Time the sweep of the stick to ½ second— 10 sweeps every 5 seconds—and then observe the distance between the phantom sticks. (See illustration on page 128.)

If the end of the stick is made to sweep through 5 feet in ½ second, its speed is 10 feet a second. If the space between the phantom sticks is one inch, it is quite easy to see that there are 60 in half a second, or 120 a second. This means that the moving stick is illuminated 120 times a second. From the sine curve you will see that there are two maxima every cycle, one positive and one negative. Thus if the stick shows up 60 times in its 5-foot sweep, that is, in ½ second, the current in the lamps has a frequency of 60 cycles a second.

This simple experiment demonstrates two important scientific

White stick swinging against a black background illuminated by alternating-current lamp appears to be several sticks. A simple method of calculating the frequency of supply.

measurements with the simplest of apparatus: the frequency of your electric supply and the measurement of a very short interval of time, $\frac{1}{120}$ second. Tests of this kind can be made with much greater precision than is possible with a swinging stick. They can be made, for example, with the *oscillograph*.

The oscillograph was invented to show exactly what is going on in an electrical circuit when the action is too rapid for the eye to follow. It is a kind of time microscope which stretches out small fractions of a second to such a size that they can be dealt with comfortably.

There are two main kinds of oscillograph: the electromagnetic type and the cathode-ray type. The electromagnetic oscillograph is simply a quick-acting galvanometer. The ordinary galvanometer arrives at its conclusions in rather a slow fashion, but for accurate measurements an instrument is needed that can indicate the current passing through it within a fraction of a second, and it must be able to change its mind just as quickly as the current changes its mind. It must draw a curve in a way that will show, in magnified form, all the changes that take place during the shortest possible intervals which cannot be followed with the unaided eye.

The construction of the electromagnetic oscillograph follows that of the ordinary galvanometer or ammeter. It has a magnet with a powerful magnetic field between its adjacent poles, and in this space is suspended a coil carrying the current to be investigated. To make it move quickly the coil is very lightly constructed of a single loop of very fine phosphor bronze strip. To keep it lively the loop is kept under tension by the pull of a spring. No pointer is used; this would make the instrument too sluggish. Instead, a beam of light acts as a pointer. The coil carries a tiny mirror, and from a distance a lamp sheds a ray of light onto the mirror. This is reflected onto a revolving drum of sensitive paper as a curve. Thus the sine curve, or any other curve, can be reproduced rapidly and examined at leisure afterward.

When the curve is being repeated time after time, it can be examined by eye through an ingenious attachment: the beam of light leaving the vibrating mirror is made to fall on another mirror which is kept rotating at right angles. This second mirror deflects the beam sideways and, as it is being constantly repeated in the same place on the screen, we can watch the shape with ease. This is called the *stationary trace*. With such an instrument the wave of an alternating current can be recorded up to thousands of cycles a second.

The second type of oscillograph, the cathode-ray oscillograph, operates even faster than the electromagnetic type. In fact, it can follow changes of millions of cycles a second. This can be expressed as a "writing speed," or the speed at which the spot moves across the scale, which may be as much as ten thousand miles a second. The cathode-ray oscillograph depends on the working of the free electron (see chapter 11). The oscillograph's trace is produced by a stream of electrons hitting a sensitive screen and making a bright spot which moves about at incredible speeds.

No discussion of these instruments for demonstrating wave shapes is complete without reference to the subject of rectification. When direct current is required for special purposes—as, for instance, charging a battery or running a subway train— we can use AC and employ a device called a *rectifier,* which converts AC into DC. The principle of the rectifier is similar to the one-way turnstile at the amusement park. By some mechanical gadget the *in* turnstile will only go forward, and when you come out of the show the *out* turnstile will not let you in again.

In the rectifier this process is done electrically. If the current is to flow in the direction of the upper part of the sine curve, a door, so to speak, is inserted in the circuit, which only opens in that direction. AC passes through the door, grows during a small fraction of a second to a maximum, and then falls off to zero again. It tries to turn back for the lower half cycle but the door closes in its face. The result is that the curve of current, cycle after cycle, has humps interspersed with blank spaces. For half the cycle the current flows and then for the other half of the cycle there is no current. The next time around the current flows once more and so on. We thus have a direct current, always in the same direction, but intermittent.

For instance, suppose 100 people were to line up at a turnstile, 50 already beyond the stile and 50 waiting to pass through. Then suppose the man at the gate were to adjust the mechanism on the turnstile so that it will go either way. At the word "March" everybody walks toward the fair grounds. At

"About face" everybody walks away from the fair grounds. If the order is repeated every half minute, what has been produced? An alternating current of people passing back and forth through the turnstile.

Suppose, while half are inside and half outside, the gateman adjusts the mechanism so that it will admit people but refuse them exit. "March," and the line will advance, but at a reverse order, when everyone turns around, the turnstile will stick and nobody can move out. If, after the usual half minute, an order is given to "About face," they start off again and, as more people enter the grounds, the line moves forward.

When the turnstile admits in both directions, the current, or flow, of people moves both back and forth, in and out of the grounds. When it admits in one direction only, the "rectifier"— for that is what the turnstile now becomes—allows only forward movement and the procession moves and stops, moves and stops, but always in the one direction, inward.

Various electrical devices act as rectifiers. The first is the commutator. The next is the metal rectifier which is surprisingly simple and depends on the fact that, when a sheet of copper has one side coated with copper oxide, the current finds it much easier to travel from the oxide to the copper than from the copper to the oxide. It is as though there were a one-way door or turnstile in the molecules at the junction of the two. For a practical rectifier a number of such copper disks oxidized on one side and plain on the other are built up like a voltaic cell, with connecting disks of lead between one plate and the next. For convenience, in a diagram we represent the copper plate by a short straight line and the copper oxide by a solid arrow pointing at the plate.

When a simple unit rectifier is used that catches the AC in only one direction, it is called *half-wave* rectification, but when special circuits are set up to capture the AC in both directions, they are referred to as *full-wave* rectification. We do not want DC that is intermittent, in which only one half wave of AC is let through. We prefer to use both the positive and the negative half waves, and an ingenious device has been invented to permit this. In chapter 4 a famous circuit was described known as the Wheatstone bridge, in which a number of conductors were arranged as a diamond. If we take four simple rectifiers and arrange them in the form of a bridge, *P, Q, R,* and *S,* and connect the AC to the top and bottom terminals, we can draw off a continuous DC from the two other terminals. Notice that the two rectifiers in the arms *P* and *R* of the bridge are arranged to open the doors downward and those in arms *Q* and *S* open the doors upward. Now suppose a positive half wave of AC comes along pushing downward from *W* to *Z.* It can go to *Z* via *P,* through the DC circuit, through the battery or whatever it is we are charging, back to *Y,* through *R* to *X* and home again. At this stage *Q* and *S* say "no road." Now the AC reverses and tries to come in at *X* but this time *R* refuses admission. Door *S* is open and the battery receives the current, again in the

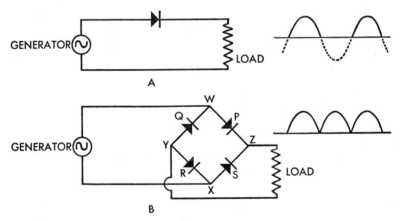

Rectification of alternating current. (A) Half-wave rectification: opposite half wave cut out. (B) Full-wave rectification by use of four rectifiers in the form of a Wheatstone bridge.

right direction, and it passes on to Y through Q, now open to W, and back again. W and X are the incoming AC terminals and Y and Z the outgoing rectified DC terminals.

Metal rectifiers are not suitable for very heavy direct currents such as are required for railways and industrial purposes; in these instances an entirely different kind of rectifier is used, known as the *mercury arc rectifier.* In large industrial plants you will sometimes see these strange-looking devices made of glass blown into grotesque shapes with pools of agitated mercury and "perspiring" beads of mercury on the inside surface of the glass wall. They are filled with an unearthly flickering and an intense pale-blue light. They are usually hidden behind iron screens, but anyone in the electrical engineering field will tell you where one can be seen. Unfortunately for the romantic side of the story of electricity, the open-glass type is being replaced, particularly in the larger sizes, by the metal-tank type which is not half so interesting to watch.

The operation of the mercury arc rectifier depends on the fact that if we have a pool of mercury in a container from which the air has been extracted and an iron or carbon anode is passed through the container above the mercury, current will flow easily from the anode to the mercury but not in the opposite direction. Again, as in the case of the metal rectifier, the use of one mercury arc rectifier will stop only one half of the sine wave and the DC we get will have gaps at every half cycle of the AC. It will produce direct, or unidirectional, current but not continuous current.

There are several ways to avoid this intermittent feature in the DC. The simplest way is to use two anodes in the same rectifier bulb. During one half cycle the current flows from one anode to the pool of mercury, and in the second half cycle from the other anode to the pool and so maintains the required unidirectional current on the output.

Another type of rectifier which has assumed great importance is the *germanium* rectifier. Slices from a crystal of pure germanium are provided with soldered terminals on opposite faces, and the barrier layer inside the crystal is so effective that current travels 400,000 times more easily in one direction than in the opposite direction. This is a great advance over other rectifiers, particularly as very heavy currents can be carried by such rectifiers.

In addition to the commutator, the metal rectifier, the germanium rectifier and the mercury arc rectifier, there are other methods of obtaining DC from AC, but they are of less importance than the ones described. However, there is one method that is very important—the method which uses the thermionic vacuum tube. The principle employed and the method of application, however, place the thermionic vacuum tube in an entirely different branch of electrical engineering and we shall defer the discussion of it until we come to the chapter on the free electron (chapter 11).

The word *synchronize* is of considerable importance and significance in alternating current engineering. We know the word in everyday life; when two events happen at the same time, we say they synchronize. We press the button and the bell rings, or by a curious coincidence the mail arrives three days running just as we finish breakfast. These are events which synchronize, they happen together. In the use of alternating currents synchronism goes a stage further; it is not just one pair of events coming together. It is the continually repeated running together of events. An electric clock is a good example. If the clock mechanism synchronizes with the frequency of the power supply and if the generator speed at the power station is properly controlled, our electric clocks give the correct time. Clocks which depend on the steady frequency of the electric supply are known as synchronous clocks; and, to be of any use, they must be connected to a system which is time-controlled by a master clock.

A synchronous clock has a synchronous motor, one that is driven by AC and runs at a definite speed locked into the frequency of the supply. This is quite different from DC motors (see chapter 5). DC motors slow down when the load is increased, as with the electric train approaching a hill. But the AC synchronous motor maintains the same speed no matter how the load is increased. If we try to get too much out of the motor, it suddenly falls out of synchronism and stops.

In a DC motor the direction of current in the armature windings has to be reversed during the revolution. As the armature passes one pole of the magnet, it must be made to attract the opposite pole which follows. This reversal is done by a commutator. In the AC synchronous motor the reversal comes about by the alternation of the current itself. In the DC motor the commutator must reverse the current at just the correct moment and must therefore be fixed rigidly to the spindle. A DC motor would never work if the commutator were loose on the spindle and slipped back and forth out of control. The same factor controls the AC synchronous motor—the alternations of the supply current must be precisely in step with the rotation of the motor.

Synchronism can be understood by studying the construction of a simple electric clock. In an ordinary electric clock the rotating part consists of a wheel, or rotor, made of magnet steel, with projecting arms which are magnetized alternately north and south. The stator, in the form of a surrounding ring, is made in two parts which clamp together, each with a series of sideways projections, and a circular core common to the two sides. When a current is passed through the coil it produces north magnetic poles on all the projections on one side and south magnetic poles on all the projections on the other side. Thus the inner surface exposed to the rotating wheel has alternate north

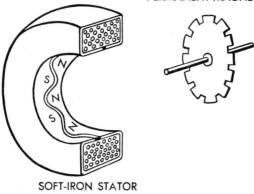

PERMANENT-MAGNET ROTOR

SOFT-IRON STATOR

Principles of synchronous AC motor illustrated by the electric clock motor. The soft-iron casing surrounding a main coil has a wavy open joint. When a current flows in the coil, alternate projections become north and south poles. With AC the poles change with the alternations and pull around the magnetized stator at the correct speed.

and south poles when a steady current is applied to the coil.

When, however, the coil is supplied with AC, these alternate poles keep on changing, all the north poles change to south poles, and all the south poles change to north poles, and they keep doing this at the supply frequency—60 times a second. If the rotor is stationary it will, in the ordinary course, remain stationary. The speed of the changes is too much for it. At one moment all its north poles will be attracted by the south poles on the surrounding stator and it will try to start off in that direction but, long before it has begun to move, the south poles on the stator change into north poles and it is pushed back again. Suppose, now, we give the rotor a slight spin by hand. The north poles are attracted by the south poles, but just as these change to north poles the north poles on the rotor are past and are approaching the next lot which by this time are south poles. These continue the attraction and the pull remains in the same direction all the time. Most modern clocks are made self-starting by the introduction of a rotating winding which brings them up to the synchronous speed.

If we spin the rotor by hand at what is called synchronism speed, whenever the attraction in the right direction ceases it begins again at the pole beyond. The pull continues as before, and so we obtain continuous motion. The clock continues to run in synchronism.

Synchronizing is of very great importance in power stations. When a number of alternators in the same or in different power stations are connected in parallel, each one contributing its share of the load, it is most essential that they should all produce their individual currents at the same frequency. There would be hopeless confusion, and considerable damage to the plant, if one machine tried to send current into the lines at a frequency of 58 cycles a second and another at 62 cycles a second. They must all be in step at 60 cycles a second.

And there is another condition. Suppose that on the stroke of midnight machine A is running at 60 cycles a second, and that its sine curve is just starting off from zero in the positive direction. Suppose, further, that machine B also is running exactly at 60 cycles a second but that it is running $\frac{1}{240}$ second (a quarter of a cycle) late. Imagine what will happen at that moment $\frac{1}{240}$ second after midnight. Machine A is giving full voltage and machine B no voltage at all. A very heavy short-circuit current will flow from machine A into the windings of machine B and cause damage.

The conditions will be worse still if machine B is running half a cycle, or $\frac{1}{120}$ second, late. Look at the two sine curves illustrated on page 138. Alternator A is now at its maximum in the positive direction and alternator B is at its maximum in the negative direction. If the switch connecting the two machines is closed under these conditions there will be an explosion, the station superintendent, if he is still alive, will think an atom

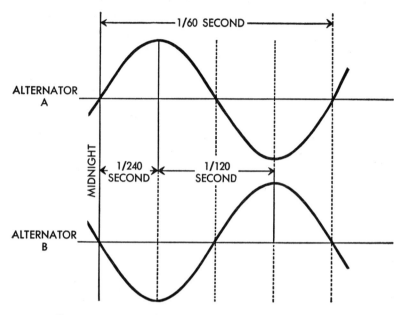

Sine curves of two alternators out of phase with each other.

bomb has hit the place, and there'll be no light in the neighborhood for some time to come. The machines were coupled together "out of phase" and will be destroyed by the resulting
enormous current that will flow between them.

For this reason when AC generators are coupled together or
are to be brought onto the power lines, they must first be
synchronized to run at exactly the correct speed, and they must
be exactly "in phase." To insure that these conditions are met,
various methods are employed. A simple device uses lamps
connected between one terminal of the incoming alternator and
the corresponding bus bar. If the alternator is running at the
correct speed and, therefore, giving the correct voltage and is
in the correct phase, the lamps will not light as, of course, the
alternators, when in parallel on the bus bars, are in opposition
to one another. When synchronizing conditions are correct,

there is no difference of potential at any single moment between the terminal of the incoming alternator and the bus bar which it is to be connected to. Under the dangerous condition we envisaged just after midnight, the test lamps would light up brilliantly and warn us against closing the main switch.

The lamps have to be suitable for double working voltage because, when the incoming alternator is quite out of phase, the lamps are subjected to the two voltages added together. In practice the incoming machine would be running either a little too fast or a little too slow and in these circumstances the lamps would go on and off intermittently. By adjusting the speed of the machine, we can reduce the frequency of these beats and lengthen the intervals of darkness. When steady conditions have been reached, the main switch can safely be closed during the dark interval and the incoming machine then "locks" into the system, or is synchronized, and continues to supply its share of the load smoothly. It stays locked in automatically because if it did not then current would flow into it from the other alternators and it would run as a synchronous motor. The turbine driving it would be doing no work and the governors would increase the steam.

In view of the importance of satisfactory synchronization of alternators and the serious results of a mistake, many special instruments have been devised for checking synchronization. These are known as synchroscopes. In one form the instrument has a pointer moving over a circular scale which indicates the amount by which a machine is out of phase. This is watched so that the switch can be closed when the pointer is at zero. In other forms the indication is given by red and green lamps.

In discussing AC we have tended to restrict ourselves to power frequencies of 60 cycles a second and to the pure sine wave. We shall see when we come to telephone and radio applications that frequencies vary over a very wide range in the many applications of alternating current. In telephone circuits the frequency may be as low as 20 per second in the deep notes of a man's voice, and as high as several thousand, approaching the upper limit which the ordinary person can detect. Dogs can receive still higher frequencies and can be called by a whistle which is inaudible to human beings. In certain industrial processes, such as the operation of furnaces, the frequency of the current may reach 100,000 cycles a second, or 100 kilocycles, and in radio work we go up to 30 million kilocycles a second and more.

One of the most important components of electrical engineering is the *transformer.* AC and the transformer go together. Transformers will not work on DC, and without transformers AC would have very little practical application.

Although transformers are now made and used in a multitude of shapes and sizes for many purposes, they are really simple devices and work on a simple principle. If two coils of wire are near one another and an alternating current is passed through one, an alternating current is induced in the other. Or to be more precise, an alternating voltage is induced in the second, which will result in an alternating current when the circuit is closed.

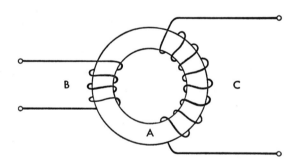

The three main parts of a transformer. (A) Iron core. (B) Primary coil. (C) Secondary coil. Set-up ratio 2 to 1.

This is because the primary coil generates an alternating magnetic field in its neighborhood and these lines of force embrace the secondary coil where they generate a voltage. In Faraday's original coil which led him to the discovery of the transformer, the two windings—primary and secondary—were wound on an iron ring. Faraday puzzled long over the connection between electricity and magnetism before he discovered the way to generate a current by thrusting a magnet into a coil of wire (chapter 6). This was on October 17, 1831. A few months earlier, on August 29, 1831, he had devised the transformer and the notes he made are worth repeating:

Experiments on the production of Electricity from Magnetism, etc. etc. Have had an iron ring made (soft iron), iron round and 6 inches in external diameter. Wound many coils of copper wire round, one half the coils being separated by twine and calico—there were 3 lengths of wire each about 24 feet long and they could be connected as one length or used as separate lengths. By trial with a trough each was insulated from the other. Will call this side of the ring A. On the other side but separated by an interval was wound wire in two pieces together amounting to about 60 feet in length the direction being as with the former coils. This side call B.

Charged a battery of 10 pairs of plates 4 inches square. Made the coil on B side one coil and connected its extremities by a copper wire passing to a distance just over a magnetic needle (3 feet from iron ring) then connected the ends of one of the pieces on A side with battery. Immediately a sensible effect on needle. It oscillated and settled at last in original position. On breaking connection of A side with battery, again a disturbance of the needle.

Made all the wires on A side one coil and sent current from battery through the whole. Effect on needle much stronger than before.

The effect on the needle then but a very small part of that which the wire communicating directly with the battery could produce.

Faraday discovered the method by which electrical effects could be transmitted from one circuit to another via a magnetic link between the two. His experiment only led him to the intermittent effect obtained by pushing in the magnet and getting a kick on his galvanometer. He did not realize the enormous value his results would subsequently attain when the primary coil was supplied with an alternating current and a new current was taken from the secondary. By this application we now have one of the most useful pieces of equipment available for all branches of electrical work.

Transformers are made in many different forms and sizes, depending on the uses to which they are to be put, but their chief use is for changing voltage. The voltage is proportional to the number of turns in the two windings. If a transformer has 100 turns of wire on the primary and 1,000 on the secondary, we get ten times increase in the voltage: 100 volts AC applied to the primary will produce 1,000 volts AC in the secondary. This is called a step-up transformer but we can use it in the opposite direction equally well. We can call the coil with the 1,000 turns the primary, apply 1,000 volts AC to it and draw off AC at 100 volts from the low-voltage secondary. When it is used in this way it is called a step-down transformer.

In a step-up transformer finer wire is used in the secondary winding than in the primary because it has to carry less current. If the ratio of voltage is 1 to 10, then the ratio of current is 10 to 1. A transformer fed, for example, with 50 amperes on the primary side at a voltage of 100 volts would give out only 5 amperes at 1,000 volts on the secondary side. It is for this reason that step-up transformers are usually employed: by raising the voltage supplied by an alternator they enable the load to be carried by a smaller conductor over a long distance. (This will be considered later in discussing transmission.) When a very heavy alternating current is required, a step-down transformer is used and the output current, although at a low voltage, may be thousands of amperes.

The main parts of a typical power transformer are magnetic core, windings, container with cooling oil, and insulators. To reduce the eddy currents and consequent heating due to the rapidly changing magnetization, the core is built up of thin sheets of soft iron, called laminations, which are lightly insulated from each other by a coating of varnish or very thin paper. The structure is bolted rigidly together, and considerable ingenuity is displayed in constructing the coils so that, on the one hand, they resist the forces tending to move them when heavy currents pass through them and, on the other, allow space for circulation of cooling oil between them. The core with its coils is immersed in a large iron tank filled with oil, which insulates as well as cools. The ends of the coils are brought out through porcelain insulators for external connection, and on the high-voltage side very large insulators are necessary to prevent flashover from the hot wire to the ground.

In the running of DC motors the machine has a capacity for adjusting itself. When the load is applied, the speed falls, dropping the back emf, or voltage, and this in turn allows more current to flow in to meet the requirements. In a somewhat similar way a transformer is obligingly convenient. When no load is being taken from the secondary side, the primary current produces a big magnetic field in the iron core. This reacts on the primary winding and causes a choking effect which prevents the current from entering. This is the principle of the operation of a choke coil used in radio and other circuits even when there is no secondary coil.

In a simple coil of wire wound on an iron core, the magnetic field created by the current in the turns of wire reacts on the turns and generates an opposing voltage in them. Thus the coil opposes the flow of the current and is known as a *choke*. The choke effect can be demonstrated by taking a length of wire connected in series with a lamp and then coiling it around an iron rod. When the wire is straight, the lamp lights up brilliantly, but with exactly the same length of wire in the form of a choke, the lamp is dimmed because of the opposition of the choke to the passage of the current.

We normally speak of the *resistance* of a wire to the passage of a current, but in AC circuits we must also speak of another feature called the *inductance*. A straight wire has a low inductance and does not offer much opposition to the flow. A coiled wire, particularly on an iron core, offers high inductance and so chokes back the current.

When no current is taken from the secondary side of a transformer with two windings, it acts just like a choke. But when current is drawn from the secondary, this current has an influence on the magnetic field which affects the primary in such a way as to reduce the choke effect and so to increase the input of current. As a result there is complete automatic working between primary and secondary circuits. Although, electrically, they are separate, when we take more current from the secondary, more flows into the primary, and when we cut off the secondary load the primary current immediately falls to a small "no load" or, as it is called, *magnetizing* current.

Many large transformers have a series of tubes on the outside of the tank. These are only oil-cooling tubes which increase the cooling surface. Many, too, have iron cylinders on the top. These are oil cylinders, or expansion vessels, to compensate for the change in oil volume as the temperature rises and falls between full load and no load.

Some of the most spectacular transformers in use today are those designed for high-voltage testing. Because items of electrical equipment must be tested at a voltage much in excess of their working voltage, the transformers to generate these high voltages are exceptional. They are often capable of giving over a million volts and can release a noisy discharge which resembles a flash of lightning.

We have considered, so far, power transformers which are usually insulated with oil, but anyone who makes radio gadgets knows that there is another and very extensively used type of transformer field in which the windings and core are dry and exposed. At one time air cores were often employed but they have been replaced by powder coils or dust coils. Special iron of high permeability—iron which is easily magnetized—is produced in powder form. The tiny particles are surrounded by an insulating material and subjected to high pressure in a mold of the shape required. In the larger low-frequency transformers we have seen how the plates are insulated to prevent eddy currents. In radio transformers, working at much higher frequencies, this provision is even more important, and the special care taken to keep the particles of iron small and to insulate each one from its neighbor has resulted in remarkable improvement in performance. It is one of the factors which have made possible a considerable reduction in the size of radio sets.

CHAPTER 8

Light and Heat

THE simple fact that the passage of an electric current through a conductor raises its temperature has opened up a tremendous field of application. Our homes, our streets, and our workshops are lighted by electricity. Airliners fly along in the darkness with their navigation lights supplied by electricity. Inside the plane forty or fifty people enjoy a meal or read in comfort because of electricity.

The crew in a submarine carries out its duties by electric light, regulated to give degrees of intensity or dimness. The light on a miner's helmet, fed by its own battery, enables him to pinpoint the actual scene on the rock or coal face before him. From the tiny flashlight used by the doctor to examine one's throat to the most powerful searchlight, there is evidence of what electric current has done for us.

So accepted has electricity become that the old-fashioned methods are sometimes used on occasions just for fun. I was in Zurich, Switzerland, once attending the centennial celebration of the famous Polytechnique, and on this special occasion well-known electrical engineers met one another under the romantic glow of thousands of wax candles. But nobody wants to return to candles and oil lamps for everyday use. We press a switch and the room in our home or the large concert hall is filled with clean, efficient, and convenient brilliance.

146

This point was not arrived at accidentally. Thinking men carried us from Davy's arc to our present position, and among these men two are outstanding—Thomas A. Edison, the great American inventor, and Sir Joseph W. Swan, the Englishman. They both worked on the problem of the incandescent filament lamp quite independently and thousands of miles apart.

From about 1848 Swan had been experimenting with charred paper in the construction of an electric bulb, the paper strip being in the shape of a horseshoe; but, when the carbonized paper became incandescent, the oxygen in the air combined with it and the filament perished. He tried enclosing the filament in a glass bulb from which the air had been pumped out. In spite of this and many variations in the material, such as carbonized sewing thread and paper saturated with molasses or tar, the experiments failed because the vacuum was not good enough. It was only in 1865 when Hermann Sprengel, a German inventor, made a mercury vacuum pump that the way was opened. When the Sprengel pump was invented, Swan was able to take advantage of the improved vacuum obtainable and found that his filaments lasted longer. But they still wasted away.

Not to be beaten, he studied the problem diligently and then made the big discovery that, no matter how good the vacuum when the bulb was assembled, it deteriorated during life. The filament itself while burning slowly gave off air and spoiled the vacuum!

Swan found the key to the problem in 1878 and did what has been done ever since by makers of incandescent bulbs. He passed a current through the filament to make it white hot and at the same time continued to pump the air from the vacuum. In this way the air was extracted from the filament as well as from the space in the bulb, with the result that the light burned for a long period without deterioration. Moreover, the blackening of the bulb, which had been such a nuisance, disappeared and the practical filament lamp was established. The key to the big problem of the incandescent bulb was the continuation of the vacuum pumping during the first few hours of burning. In the next few months Swan delighted audiences in the north of England with demonstrations of his wonderful new source of light.

In the United States, at his famous laboratory at Menlo Park, Edison was approaching this problem by a different route. It is difficult today to appreciate the confusion in men's minds at that time over the two methods of connecting items in series or in parallel. The idea of extensive supply lines with the voltage always available for thousands of consumers to connect different kinds of current-consuming devices had not been thought of. About 1880 and earlier the dynamo was being developed in many different forms and arc lamps were connected in series, but this system was quite unsuitable for the general use of electric light by the public. What was wanted was the sub-division of the electric light, as it was called. Ridiculous as it seems to us today, a great controversy raged throughout the civilized world: some said the light could not be subdivided; some said it could. Edison quickly entered the lists on the side of those who said it could, and he was right.

Edison's solving of the problem rested on the simple idea of using a bulb which had a high resistance and a small radiating surface. This lamp took only a small current, so the subdivision problem could be solved by arranging many such lamps in parallel with one another. His first experiment was with the platinum filament but, like Swan, Edison soon changed over to the carbon filament with equally successful results. In October, 1878, Edison convinced his financial friends that the electric light for public use was established and the Edison Electric Light Company came into being. He and Swan joined in a commercial enterprise and factories for the manufacture of the carbon filament lamp sprang up on both sides of the Atlantic. Soon many homes were equipped with this new form of lighting.

From that time to the present, filament lamps have passed through an interesting stage of development. In seventy-five years the low-efficiency carbon filament with its yellowish red light has been superseded by the modern tungsten filament working at a high efficiency and giving an intense white light. Instead of a vacuum in the bulb, the modern lamp is gas filled. Gases such as argon and nitrogen do not combine with the hot tungsten filament as the oxygen in the air would do, and the presence of the gas is better than a vacuum as it discourages the evaporation of the metal at the very high temperature now commonly used.

Tungsten is used for filaments because it has the highest melting point of any known metal. The actual figure is 3,370 degrees centigrade. For comparison, copper melts at 1,083 degrees. The filament in a modern lamp is usually formed as a spiral with a view to keeping the temperature high, and often a cylindrical coil is used to intensify the effect. Such construction increases the amount of light for the same consumption of electricity by as much as 20 per cent.

The manufacturing methods by which a modern incandescent filament lamp is made are very ingenious and yet so simple that large numbers are turned out in our factories by mass-production methods. The usual type of lamp has four main parts: the bulb, the filament, the foot with filament support, and the cap. The filament is mounted on metal wire supports fused into the upper end of a central glass rod, and its ends are connected by two wire electrodes, or lead-in wires, which are fused into the glass support. These lead-in wires are made of a special metal which expands with heat at about the same rate as does glass. This prevents the glass from cracking as the lamp becomes hot.

There are many tricks of the trade in making an electric lamp but one really should be mentioned because of its ingenuity. As we saw, Swan made a great step forward in the early days by heating the filament before sealing the bulb and with the vacuum pump still applied. Today the process is speeded up by spraying the filament with a substance known as a *getter,* which consists of phosphorus and other materials. When the filament is heated, the getter evaporates and carries with it the unwanted last traces of gas, so adding greatly to the life of the lamp.

Although we continue to use filament lamps in our homes, on our automobiles, and for a large number of other purposes, there is an increasing number of lamps which have no filament. In these lamps the light originates, not from a white-hot wire, but from a discharge of electricity inside a glass tube. For many years it has been known that current could be passed through a gas at a low pressure and that light of many beautiful colors could be produced. Glass tubes of curious shapes containing different gases were a popular scientific curiosity about fifty years ago and were known as Geissler tubes. Today these have developed into the many striking forms of gas-discharge lamps (or what we speak of, loosely, as neon lights), now so well known.

A wide variety of color and form is produced in these various types of electric lighting. Advertising signs are largely composed of long glass tubes bent to the desired shape and filled with the gas *neon,* which gives a brilliant red color. Other colors are possible; for instance, the gas helium gives pink and a mixture of neon, argon, and mercury gives a blue light.

A feature which distinguishes neon-sign tubes from other forms of discharge lamps is the fact that they require a high voltage, something like 6,000 volts. If you examine such a sign from the street you can see the small transformers provided for raising the power supply voltage to this value. You can often see a switch with a handle which can be reached from the street by a pole called the "fireman's switch." When fire engines arrive at the scene of a fire, the firemen switch off the neon signs quickly; otherwise the men might get an electric shock through the jet of water.

The use of the neon light is restricted almost entirely to advertising and display purposes. For real illumination two other kinds of gas-discharge lamps have made great headway during the past few years and are now well known because of the characteristic color which they emit: these are the sodium lamp and the mercury-vapor lamp.

The sodium lamp gives a striking yellow light. In Europe it is used for lighting highways. It consists of a glass tube with metal electrodes sealed into each end of the tube; inside is a quantity of the metal sodium which gives off a vapor through which the brilliant yellow discharge takes place. When the sodium is cold, the ordinary voltage is insufficient to start the discharge. The lamp has to be warmed up, and this is done by adding a quantity of rare gas to bring about ignition. The gas is usually neon with perhaps a little argon added.

Why do sodium lamps burn red when first switched on in the evening? The reason is that at first the discharge is due to the neon and is red; it takes a few minutes for the tube to warm up and for the yellow sodium discharge to take over. Sodium lamp tubes are usually made in a *U* shape so that the two terminals come close together for convenience in connecting. In order to prevent their being unduly chilled on exposure to the weather, the tubes are enclosed in a further outside glass tube with a vacuum between which prevents the escape of heat. Sodium lamps are being used extensively for approach lighting on airports so that the pilot coming in at night has a clear pattern leading him down to the runway.

There are also lamps which give an intense bluish white light. These are mercury-vapor lamps. They are widely used for lighting large offices and manufacturing plants, airport hangars, etc. This, again, is a gas-discharge lamp and the gas is provided by the evaporation of a small quantity of mercury in the tube.

Both the sodium lamp and the mercury-vapor lamp have limitations. Because of the color of the light they are not suitable for many situations where the filament lamp with its more comfortable light is used.

Light comes to us in the form of tiny waves in space, much too small to be seen separately. They are easily distinguished by the sensitive screen, called the retina, at the back of our eyes which transmits the sensation of light to our brain. The effect depends on the lengths of these tiny waves, because waves of one wave length produce the sensation of one color and waves of another wave length, another color. For example, when there are about 25,000 waves to the inch we get the sensation of red and when about 35,000 the sensation is blue.

Many of you will have experimented with a glass prism and seen the beautiful range of colors that emerge when daylight passes through the prism. You have noticed, too, the flashing colors which come from a diamond or, to take a very different example, from thin layers of oil floating on water. In all these examples the white daylight is split up into its many components and each of them consists of light of a definite wave length. If we place the different colors in order of wave length, we get the well-known visible spectrum: red, orange, yellow, green, blue, indigo, and violet.

As the wave length gets longer, we move toward the red end of the spectrum. "What happens beyond?" you ask. There are light waves longer than the red waves but our eyes cannot follow them. We call the region *infrared,* and at the other end, where the waves get shorter and shorter, we enter the *ultraviolet* region, again beyond our power of seeing.

The character Å is the unit (the angstrom unit) for measuring wave lengths of light and is named for the Swedish inventor A. J. Ångström. We measure the length of a table in feet, but we measure the wave lengths of light in angstroms. The red wave is about 7,000 Å long, and the blue about 5,000 Å. There are 100 million angstroms in a centimeter.

When the electric discharge takes place in a space where there is one substance, the wave length of the light produced is limited. Different gases give different colors: neon, red; sodium, yellow; and so on. The mercury-vapor lamp produces quite a lot of light outside the visible range, with a wave length less than 4,000 Å. Light of this kind is called ultraviolet light, meaning beyond the violet.

Ultraviolet light, the unseen light, at this end of the spectrum is more interesting than the infrared at the other end. For one thing it is dangerous to the eyes, and special precautions have to be taken in the selection of glass for the tubes to prevent the ultraviolet radiation from escaping from such lamps. But the light can also be used in special lamps known as *black lamps*. These lamps do not give out light as lamps usually do. There is just a faint purple glow, but if we shine the black light which they emit on certain substances, these glow brightly.

These lamps are used to distinguish natural gems from artificial ones, and for examining chemical substances in the manufacture of rubber and other products. Powders which look alike in daylight are very different when viewed under ultraviolet light; one will be cream colored, another pink, and so on. Such lights are often used to produce stage effects in theaters. Objects partially covered with a coating of fluorescent substance are invisible until the black light is thrown on them; then the painted parts glow brightly and the unpainted parts remain black.

The greatest triumph in modern electric lighting is the fluorescent lamp. This lamp is a gas-discharge lamp but, unlike the other gas-discharge lamps, its illuminating properties do not alone come from the lighting up of the gas. Quite a different principle is involved. The lamps are arranged so that the discharge produces ultraviolet light, and this in turn causes fluorescence of specially selected substances coated on the inside of the tube. These glow and emit the required light.

The solid materials which fluoresce, or become luminous when ultraviolet light is played on them, are called *phosphors:* magnesium tungstate, cadmium, cadmium borate, halophosphate, etc. These produce a wide range of beautiful soft colors. Much attention has been given to securing the best color rendering; sometimes a warm effect is desired and sometimes artificial daylight is wanted for matching purposes. Fluorescent lamps have now been developed so far that practically any special requirement can be met.

To insure the rapid ignition of a fluorescent lamp the two electrodes are often made in the form of a small coiled filament of tungsten wire. The circuit is such that when the lamp is switched on cold, current passes through the filaments and helps the discharge to start. As soon as the discharge begins, the current in the filament is interrupted by a thermally operated switch. The discharge is assisted by a coating of special oxides on the filament, and in the cold-cathode lamp now available it is no longer necessary to heat the electrodes for starting up. The diagram that shows the arrangement also shows the choke, an iron-cored coil, which limits the current when the lamp is burning.

At the beginning of this chapter we saw how the heating effect of an electric current in a wire was used in the production of the filament lamp, opening up a vast field of electric lighting. We shall now take a look at another field in which the heating property is utilized.

By means of electricity our homes and offices can be heated

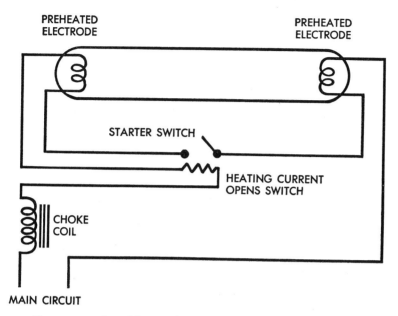

PREHEATED
ELECTRODE

PREHEATED
ELECTRODE

STARTER SWITCH

HEATING CURRENT
OPENS SWITCH

CHOKE
COIL

MAIN CIRCUIT

Fluorescent tube, with one of many arrangements for starting the discharge.

efficiently and conveniently with a minimum of labor. In our industrial plants electric furnaces melt steel in huge vessels from which it can be poured like water, while small metal components for machines or tools are made red hot in a few seconds for annealing purposes. In medicine, electricity is used for its curative properties, and in these and many other ways the production of heat from electricity is a vital factor in modern life.

In the process of converting electrical energy into heat there is an interesting theory which depends on the fact that heat and electricity are interchangeable. In most of our daily activities we are not able to relate cause and effect with great precision. We know, for instance, that there is some connection between food consumed by an athlete and his physical achievement, but we cannot say that an extra egg for breakfast will add two inches to his high jump. Converting electricity into heat is quite different. We know before we start what the effect will be if we understand the rules.

There is a special language for dealing with electrical energy and with heat energy. In the electric circuit we speak of *units* of electrical energy; the unit is the quantity we read on the dials of our electricity meter. A one-kilowatt electric heater uses just one unit of electric energy every hour. If such a heater is supplied at a voltage of 100 and takes a current of 10 amperes, the power is 1000 watts (100 × 10), or one *kilowatt*. When a power of one kilowatt is used continuously for one hour the amount of energy consumed is one *kilowatt-hour*.

What about the heat output? Heat energy is measured by its effect on the temperature of a known quantity of water. One unit of heat will raise the temperature of a small quantity of water many degrees, or of a large quantity a few degrees. There are two different units of heat, depending on whether you measure weight in pounds and temperature in degrees Fahrenheit or weight in grams and temperature in degrees centigrade. On the continent of Europe and in scientific circles, grams and degrees centigrade are used. In the United States pounds and degrees Fahrenheit are more usual in practice.

The heat needed to raise the temperature of one gram of water from 0° C to 1° C is called a *calorie*. Similarly, the heat needed to raise the temperature of one pound of water one degree Fahrenheit is called a *British thermal unit* (BTU). There are 453.5 grams in a pound, and a rise of 1° F equals a rise of ⅝° C.

$$1 \text{ BTU} = 252 \text{ calories}$$

As the result of many experiments in converting electricity into heat, it is now known that one kilowatt-hour is equal to 3420 BTU, or about 860,000 calories.

All of this arithmetic can be useful. Suppose you want to make coffee for 100 people at a party. You have rented an electric coffee maker for the purpose. How long beforehand must the coffee maker be switched on?

First, you examine the plate on the coffee maker, which states the power taken. Let's suppose it is 5 kw. Although the coffee maker will take 10 gallons of water, it is estimated that you will need only 8 gallons of boiling water to start with. By applying a power of 5 kw, how long will it take to raise the temperature of 8 gallons of water from, say, 52° F to 212° F, an increase of 160° F?

A gallon of water weighs 10 pounds. The number of BTU required is $8 \times 10 \times 160$ (the pounds multiplied by the temperature rise). This number is divided by 3,420 and you get the number of kw-hr required. If you divide again by 5, because you will have 5 kw of energy going into the water every hour, and multiply by 60, you will get a figure for the time in minutes.

$$\frac{8 \times 10 \times 160 \times 60}{3,420 \times 5} = \text{approximately 45 minutes.}$$

Remember that while the temperature of the water is being raised some of the heat will escape by radiation and there will be some cooling because of drafts. To be on the safe side, you had better apply what the engineer calls "a factor of safety," and advise switching on the current an hour before the coffee is to be made.

While we are on the subject of water heating, we should examine some of the more common devices used for the purpose. To avoid throwing excessive loads on the electric circuit for short periods it is usual in employing electricity for heating water to use what are called "thermal" storage heaters. The water is not heated only as and when required but is brought up to the required temperature slowly—sometimes over several hours—and then stored hot ready for use.

To heat enough water for a bath at about 140° F while you are impatiently waiting for, say, 3 minutes might require nearly 100 kw. With a storage heater having a loading of only 3 kw spread over 1½ to 2 hours, you could produce all the hot water necessary for a deep bath and fill the tub in a very few minutes.

Water heaters are fitted with *thermostats* which automatically control the temperature. There are many different types of electrical thermostats used for this and other purposes, and the construction varies widely. In the stem type a rod of special metal, such as Invar, which does not expand with increase of temperature, is enclosed in a tube of another metal, brass or bronze, which has a high coefficient of expansion. At one end they are connected and at the other end are separated. When the whole assembly gets hot, the tube expands over the projecting end of the inner rod and the movement is made to operate a switch which opens the circuit under control. As the temperature falls, following the switching off of the current, the tube contracts and once more closes the switch. In this way the thermostat keeps the temperature constant within narrow limits.

Another type of thermostat depends on the use of a bimetallic strip. This has two different metals in one strip; as the temperature changes, the strip bends, due to the one metal expanding and contracting more than the other. Such thermostats are used for controlling room temperatures either by switching electric heating units or by operating hot-water or steam valves. Because of their simple form and small dimensions they are also used extensively in electric irons.

Provision is made in the domestic storage heater for avoiding the building up of steam pressure inside. One system, known as the *displacement* system, enables the user to turn on the water by opening a valve that supplies water to the heater from the main. The cold water enters the heater and displaces the already-heated water, which escapes from the open outlet into the sink or bathtub. In the pressure system, when one electric water heater feeds several faucets in the house, provision is made for preventing dangerous pressures by having an open-ended pipe carried up to the highest point of the house.

Another well-known piece of electrical equipment found in nearly every home is the electric iron. It has a polished sole plate on which is laid the heating element, consisting of a special alloy resistance wire (nickel-chromium) wound on strips of mica and sandwiched in between an upper and a lower mica sheet for insulating purposes. To prevent burning of the fabric by over-heating, most electric irons contain a simple thermostat to limit the temperature. In many designs a control knob allows the thermostat to be adjusted at will for different materials being ironed.

Electric heat has certain advantages over other forms of heat, such as cleanliness, convenience of control, facility of application, and so on. In no sphere are these advantages more evident than in the application of electric heat to the cooking of food. Through the electric toaster we are able to bring right to the table a process which not many years ago involved sitting over an open fire with the slice of bread impaled on a toasting fork. In the usual form of electric toaster the resistance wires of nickel-chromium are open-wound on mica strips. The usual loading for a home toaster is about 750 to 1000 watts but larger ones are made for restaurants. These toast both sides of the bread at once and are usually automatic, delivering the toast continuously as it is finished. In modern domestic toasters of the pop-up type the automatic operation is performed by a bimetallic strip which ejects the toast when it is ready.

The electric range is nowadays a most important component of the modern kitchen. It usually consists of a roasting oven fitted with heating elements in the side walls or in the top and bottom, and a series of boiling plates on the outside top surface. There is also usually a grill which may be separate or combined with one of the boiling plates. Various kinds of heating elements are used in different ranges and indeed in different parts of the same range.

In the oven the elements may consist of coiled wires carried in a refractory base similar to those in the open electric heater, or in the form of a tubular element. The latter consists of a non-ferrous tube about the diameter of a lead pencil in which a spiral of resistance wire is embedded in a mineral insulating material well packed in. For oven cooking, black heat is required and the elements do not glow.

Boiling plates on electric ranges are of two distinct kinds. In the older enclosed or solid type the boiling pan stands on the plain ground upper surface of the boiling plate, the underside of which is grooved to take the heating wires embedded in mineral insulating material. These plates work at a dull heat and their efficiency depends on a close contact with the boiling pan, which must therefore have a ground flat bottom. The chief disadvantage of this type of boiling plate is the long time taken to heat up and cool down. To overcome this disadvantage the radiant boiling plate has now been widely adopted. In this type the live wire is encased in a tubular element. This construction eliminates the risk of electric shock by contact with open wires. Boiling plates may have loadings of under a kilowatt, or may exceed two kilowatts; while, for speedy heating up, oven elements may have a total of up to two kilowatts as a maximum, although after the first fifteen minutes or so only 500 watts may be required to supply the losses.

From electric ranges we go to industrial electric furnaces. There are many different kinds of electric furnaces in use today, especially for smelting aluminum and iron. Furnaces required for melting metals employ powerful arcs between huge carbon rods which project through the cover into the furnace. These are supplied with current from an adjoining transformer through flexible cables. Such furnaces take very large currents and are used extensively for steelmaking and for the production of copper. Temperatures of the arc may reach 3500° C, and charges of fifty tons and more may require electric powers of thousands of kilowatts to melt them. Not only is the electric current used as the source of heat, but complex electric circuits with motors and control mechanism are also provided, so that on completion of the melt the whole furnace can be tilted by the operation of a switch and the liquid metal poured out into molds.

In another type of electric furnace, where temperatures do not need to exceed 1400° C, the heat is generated by resistors or heating elements on the walls outside the brick-lined shell of the furnace. Special care has to be taken to employ materials which themselves do not melt at these temperatures. Alloys like nickel-chromium are very resistant to destruction, but at the higher temperature even they are unsuitable, and silicon carbide in some form is necessary. Other alternative metals are being experimented with in an effort to extend the temperature range still higher.

A third type of furnace is the induction furnace in which the heat is generated by currents flowing in the charge of metal itself. The currents are induced on the usual transformer principle from a primary winding outside the furnace. The metal to be melted acts as the secondary of the transformer. To increase the effect, high-frequency currents are used. An example of the efficiency of this high-frequency current can be seen in a crucible of metal containing one ton of steel raised to a temperature of 2000° C in under two hours with the expenditure of only 200 kilowatts. The frequency in this case was 1000 cycles per second.

Closely allied to the application of heat through the electric furnace is the use of electricity for welding. There are two different kinds: arc welding and resistance welding. Arc welding is the one best known. In this method two steel plates, or whatever are to be welded together, are brought near to one another and an electric arc is struck between the edge of the metal and a metal electrode carried by the operator who, of course, wears an eye shield.

The temperature of the plates and of the electrode rises rapidly, and globules of metal pass from the electrode and stick to the plate. If the arc is directed to the two adjacent edges of two separate plates, it fills the space between them with melted metal and welds them firmly together. Either AC or DC is used for welding, the choice between the two depending on the nature of the work. Welding of this kind is widely replacing the use of rivets for connecting items of steel such as plates and beams in ship-building and land structures.

A branch of electric welding that is finding increasing useful-ness is stud welding. In many fields of engineering it is neces-sary to provide upstanding bolts, or studs, on a steel plate for the attachment of some object: bracket, handhole cover, etc. The

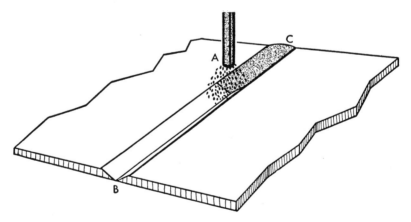

Welding steel plates together with the electric arc. (A) Special metal electrode. (B) Prepared edges of plates. (C) Completed weld.

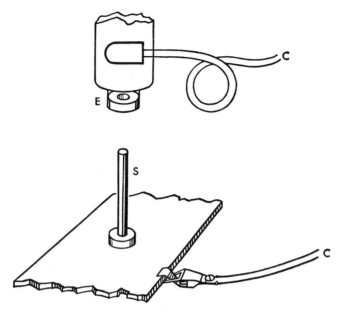

Welding steel studs onto metal plates. (S) Flat-based stud standing on plate. (E) Upper-ring electrode in pistol-form holder. (C) Cables supplying current.

old method was to drill a hole, tap a thread in the hole, and then screw in the stud.

Electric stud welding simplifies the process. The studs with flat bases and no bottom thread are held in a special electrode supplied with current through a flexible cable. After touching the plate, the stud is withdrawn a short distance. This forms an arc between the bottom of the stud and the plate, and in a fraction of a second the end of the stud and the portion of the metal plate opposite it are melted. The stud is pushed down and the current switched off. In this simple and rapid way the studs are attached without the obvious disadvantages of boring holes in the plate, and the operation is performed at ten times the former speed.

In resistance welding the parts to be welded together are

heated electrically and then pressed together mechanically. Spot welding is the usual method. A machine with two electrodes, one above the other, is operated by a pedal. Normally the electrodes remain a few inches apart while the two plates or strips are inserted between them. Pressing the pedal brings down the top electrode; current passes through the plates and makes them white hot at the point of contact; and the pressure then forces them together so that, as the current is switched off, they cool and become firmly attached to one another.

Electric current is also used for selective heating of small objects by high-frequency induction. A good example is the fixing of hard tungsten tips to lathe tools. The tip is placed in position with a brazing alloy between it and the steel, and a current at a frequency of anything up to 10 megacycles per second is passed through a specially shaped coil fitting closely around the tool but not touching it. In a flash everything is hot enough to melt the brazing material and the connection is made. This application depends on the heating caused by the eddy currents in the metal.

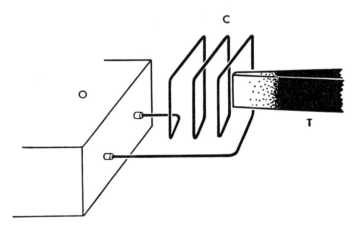

High-frequency heating used for annealing small tools. The item T *is raised to a red heat by eddy currents induced in it from a core,* C, *of a few turns which carries a current of a frequency of 100,000 cycles per second and more.* O *is the high-frequency oscillator.*

Another example is in the hardening of the surface of a steel rod or toothed wheel. A surrounding coil carrying the high-frequency current heats a skin-deep layer to 700° C and the item is dropped into water long before the remainder is even warm.

Finally, there is dielectric heating. Currents at radio frequencies up to 10 megacycles can be used to heat metals. There is a new and rapidly developing field in which nonmetallic substances are being heated by currents at even higher frequencies, up to 100 megacycles per second. In this case the object is placed in the space between two metal plates forming an air condenser and the voltage at the high frequency is applied across the plates. Something akin to molecular friction takes place throughout the mass of the material and the temperature of every part rises at once.

In modern industrial operation pellets of molding powder are heated in this way before they are placed in the molding machine. The seams of raincoats and other articles made of pvc (polyvinylchloride) are joined in this way instead of by stitching. Plastic cements in woodworking are treated by dielectric heating. Even in physiotherapy dielectric heating is used. Here the inner tissues of the body can be raised in temperature by induction rather than by transmitting heat from the outside, a much more effective treatment. Food in various forms can also be heated by this method and bread can be baked. During the next few years important developments may be expected in this field.

CHAPTER 9

The Electric Supply System

ONE of the most valuable assets of modern life is a universal, cheap, and abundant supply of electricity. We expect to find it everywhere: in our homes, our streets, our hospitals, and our offices and manufacturing plants. We cannot imagine a day without being able to press a switch to light our room, operate our radio, or work some mechanical device. We assume that the supply is available whenever required, day or night. A complex system of supply has grown up which has made all this possible.

The source of energy is coal, water power, or atomic energy. The diagram of a coal-fired powerhouse will show the process of extracting the heat from the coal, from the beginning of the process right through to the transmission of the resulting electric power over the countryside to the point where it is required for use (see pages 168–169).

The coal arrives either by rail or by water and is usually stored in vast bunkers on the ground to provide a "cushion" against fluctuating requirements. From the coal store it is carried by elevators to hoppers above the boiler house so that it can descend automatically to the boiler furnaces.

The modern steam boiler as used in electric powerhouses consists of three main parts: (1) the boiler proper, (2) the grate, or stoker, and (3) the combustion chamber. The boiler is the water-tube type and has upper and lower steel drums connected by a large number of steel tubes. The upper drum, called the *steam* drum, is usually about half full of water; the lower drum is called the *mud* drum. The water to be boiled circulates through the tubes and is heated by the hot gases passing between them.

The combustion chamber is a vast furnace lined with firebrick and, as its name implies, is the space above the burning coal where the gases combine and produce the heat. The coal is usually burned on a traveling grate at the bottom of the combustion chamber. It comes down from the hopper in a chute and forms a thick bed on the front end of the traveling grate. It is then slowly carried forward into the furnace where the heat quickly sets it afire, and by the time it reaches the far side there is nothing left but ash. This is tipped over into an ash hopper, while the grate turns over a pulley and returns underneath to the front end to begin the operation over again.

Another common method of firing a large boiler is called pulverized fuel firing. Here the coal is first ground to powder and then blown into the furnace, where the particles combine with the air and burn like a torch.

The largest of these colossal kettles is capable of boiling as much as 200 tons of water an hour; and in a station like Hell Gate, New York, where the total electrical capacity exceeds 600,000 kilowatts, there are many such boilers which altogether are capable of boiling about 3,000 tons of water an hour. This is a lot of water: it represents a pond 100 feet each way and 10 feet deep. Another interesting thing about these modern powerhouse boilers is the high temperatures and pressures at which the steam is generated. At atmospheric pressure water boils at 212° F, but temperatures of 1000° F are now common in power station boilers.

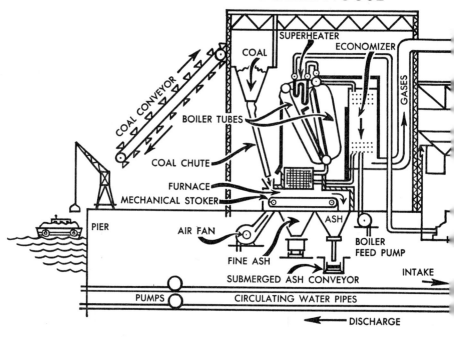

BOILER HOUSE

SUPERHEATER
ECONOMIZER
COAL
GASES
COAL CONVEYOR
BOILER TUBES
COAL CHUTE
FURNACE
MECHANICAL STOKER
PIER
AIR FAN
ASH
BOILER
FEED PUMP
FINE ASH
INTAKE
SUBMERGED ASH CONVEYOR
PUMPS
CIRCULATING WATER PIPES
DISCHARGE

The modern power station. Coal arrives on the left and is carried by conveyer to the boilers. Steam passes into the turbine house where the

At these temperatures the steam pipes begin to get red hot and have to be made of special alloy steel to prevent their bursting. Owing to the high pressure used—about a ton per square inch—the boiler cylinders have to be more than three inches thick.

These advances in temperature and pressure are for the purpose of improving the efficiency of the station. It is obviously very important to obtain as much electricity as possible for every pound of coal burned, and using hotter steam in the turbines helps this. The heating of the steam, in what is called a *superheater,* after it has left the boiler helps the efficiency too. The water

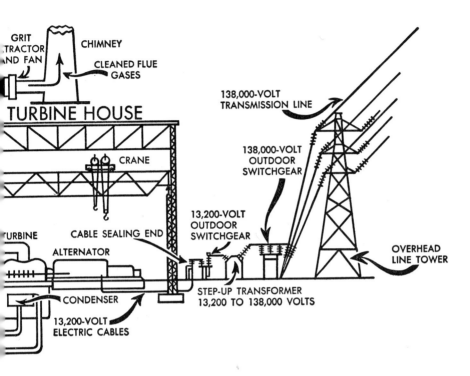

GRIT
TRACTOR
AND FAN

CHIMNEY

CLEANED FLUE
GASES

TURBINE HOUSE

CRANE

138,000-VOLT
TRANSMISSION LINE

138,000-VOLT
OUTDOOR
SWITCHGEAR

13,200-VOLT
OUTDOOR
SWITCHGEAR

TURBINE   CABLE SEALING END

ALTERNATOR

OVERHEAD
LINE TOWER

CONDENSER

STEP-UP TRANSFORMER
13,200 TO 138,000 VOLTS

13,200-VOLT
ELECTRIC CABLES

alternator generates the current. This is controlled by the switchgear on the way to the transmission line. (Adapted from Messrs. Kennedy & Donkin)

going to the boiler is heated by the escaping gases in what is called the *economizer,* a most important item in a power station. Another item of the same kind uses the gases from the fire, while they are still hot, to warm the air going into the furnace.

The outstanding impression on seeing a steam turbine for the first time is that nothing is moving. We expect an engine which is driving an electric generator to display power and movement; but here, apart from some vibration and a low-pitched rumble —and possibly a wisp of escaping steam—nothing seems to be happening. There is, of course, considerable movement in a steam turbine, but the moving parts are all enclosed. The construction consists of a central spindle extending the full length of the machine, and on this spindle there are disks of metal vanes. In the surrounding casing rings of similar vanes project inward. The disks of moving vanes on the spindle are sandwiched between the rings of fixed vanes on the casing, with only a quite small clearance space between them.

The steam entering the outer casing at one end passes along the space between the casing and the rotating part, or rotor, and in so doing threads its way through a set of fixed blades, then through a set of rotating blades, then through the next set of fixed blades, and so on. The blades are at an angle so that the effect of the steam on moving blades is to "blow" them in a circumferential direction and thus produce rotation of the spindle. The fixed blades, being set at an opposing angle, turn the steam back again so that it is ready to impinge on the next moving set. (See the diagram of a turbine on pages 120–121.)

As the steam passes through a turbine from the high pressure end to the low pressure end, it must be allowed to expand. The illustration shows how the diameter of the rotor and lengths of the blades increase along the length of the turbine, providing a greater section of space for the flow of steam as it proceeds on its journey.

There may be a problem in a steam turbine owing to the pressure of the steam tending to push the rotor along the length of the case. This problem is overcome by fixing dummy balancing pistons on the rotor spindle. By this means steam pressure introduces a balancing effect.

In the large turbines used in power stations there are usually three components: the high-pressure, the medium-pressure, and the low-pressure cylinders. The high-pressure cylinder is of small diameter and has short blades, the low-pressure cylinder is of large diameter and has long blades. The intermediate is between the two. In the low-pressure cylinder the blades are usually arranged in two separate series and the steam enters in the center space between them and escapes through the two large parts at the ends. By this arrangement the disks are self-balancing so far as longitudinal thrust is concerned and no separate balancing piston is necessary.

A man named Hero who lived in Alexandria about the time of Christ produced a simple steam turbine which actually worked. He mounted a metal ball on a spindle in bearings through which steam could be admitted to the ball, and fixed two short jets, bent over, at opposite sides of the ball for exhaust. The steam escaping from these jets pushed the ball around so that it rotated.

One of the largest and most important components in every modern power station is the condenser. It is a large ribbed iron box with one side exposed, immediately below or to the side of the turbine. The condenser receives the steam after it has passed through the turbine and condenses it into water. In the early steam engines the exhaust steam was turned loose into the open air, as is done with steam locomotives. This practice, however, was soon found to be inefficient; to get out of the engine the steam had to push its way against the pressure of the atmosphere, about 15 pounds to the square inch, and this meant an equivalent amount of effective pressure being lost in the working of the engine. In the early days of steam-engine development steam was condensed by contact with cold water passing through pipes; this produced a vacuum for the engine to discharge into.

Condensers used with turbines have hundreds of pipes about an inch in diameter through which cold water is circulated by means of a pump, and the steam is condensed in the space between the pipes. The cooling water becomes warm and is discharged into the river, or estuary, from which it has been drawn, and fresh cool water is continually drawn in. To give some idea of the quantity of water required for condensing purposes it is found that a 300,000-kilowatt station—only half the size of

Hell Gate, New York—takes 12 million gallons an hour, so a large-sized river can quickly be boiled away by a power station using it for cooling purposes.

Sometimes near certain central power stations, particularly those which are remote from estuaries or large rivers, there are vertical structures with vapor emerging from the top. These are cooling towers, used for cooling the water from the condensers. After leaving the condenser the water is allowed to trickle over an open structure of brickwork inside the tower while the natural draft of air carries away the heat and a small part of the water as vapor.

The use of cooling towers reduces the total requirements of cooling water to about one-tenth and this is important where water is scarce.

Switchgear and transformers come next in importance in the power-station layout. These control the current as it leaves the power station to start its journey along the transmission line. The actual control is not done by a man walking about in the switch yard and operating the switches. Instead, there is a control room in the power station where attendants operate the big outside switches by remote control.

Remote control in central power stations is carried out by means of electric motors or solenoids which open and close the large switches by the use of a separate current. The current is switched on or off by the attendant in the control room, as required, by means of quite small switches. There is no need to bring the heavy currents and high voltages to the point where the control is effected, which is safer and more comfortable for those concerned.

The operator is in touch with the engine-room floor and can see exactly the situation at every turbo, whether running or stationary, what voltage it is producing, and what load it is taking. He can connect it to or disconnect it from the line without leaving the control room. Having connected the generators to the bus bars, he can decide which of the several lines leaving the station shall take more or less current. In all cases, when a switch is operated, he has an up-to-date visual impression of the circuit through a "repeater" which shows the situation by means of a large circuit diagram on a wall panel. In addition to all this manual control there is a great deal of automatic control designed to protect the various items of equipment. Excessive currents in generator, cable, transformer, or line operate safety devices automatically so that, should there be an electrical fault, the particular "trip" affected is released, and in a fraction of a second the circuit is made dead before damage can be done.

Throughout the day the amount of current taken varies enormously. In the early morning it is at a minimum; when people begin to get up and switch on the current to heat their homes and begin to cook, and when electric trains begin to run and the machinery in manufacturing plants is started, the load rapidly rises. It falls off a little around midday, but there are usually two peaks, morning and afternoon, which the operator must

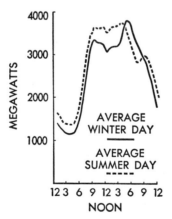

Load curves, showing the variation of the load on the station during twenty-four hours. (Adapted from Consolidated Edison Co. of New York, Inc.)

watch carefully. In order to study these fluctuations it is necessary to keep a careful record of the distribution of load. When the daily records are converted into graph form to show the picture of the load for a whole year, the graph looks like a mountain range.

We have assumed that an electric circuit consists simply of two wires, a "go" and a "return." But the transmission lines leaving the power station are different. Instead of there being two wires from one place to another there are three and sometimes six. If there are six, it is two lots of three.

When three wires (or two threes) leave a power station or a transformer substation, carried on large insulators, they are making up what is called a three-phase circuit. When alternating current is carried by two wires, a "go" and "return," the current, as we have seen, is at first nothing, then grows to a maximum value, then again falls to nothing. It then goes in the opposite direction and builds again to a maximum in that direction, falling off to zero again. The whole of the time taken to do this is called a *cycle,* and in our power supply it lasts only $\frac{1}{60}$ of a second. This is a single-phase 60-cycle current.

Three-phase current is three single-phase currents working together. Suppose we take three such circuits whose wires are *A* and *D, B* and *E, C* and *F,* and arrange them so that the wires *A, B,* and *C* are in a triangular formation and *D, E,* and *F* are close together. We could then transmit the power quite simply by sending some of it through wires *A* and *D,* some of it through wires *B* and *E,* and the rest by wires *C* and *F.* If the total current was, say, 300 amperes, then each of the three pairs of wires would carry 100 amperes—100 out and 100 back. Note carefully that wires *D, E,* and *F* would be bringing back the 300 amperes which went out on *A, B,* and *C.*

It is troublesome to imagine what goes on in a fraction of a second so we will magnify time. Let us assume that our alternat-

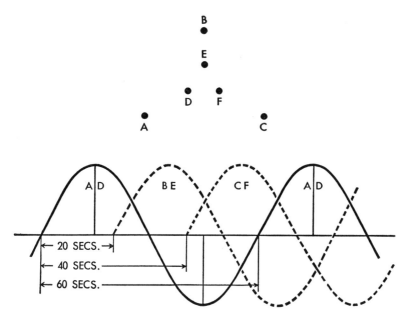

Three-phase current transmission. We imagine three separate circuits: AD, BE, CF, *each carrying 60-cycle alternating current. By drawing a vertical line through the three curves at any point and measuring the heights of the curves above the horizontal line (the outgoing current) and those below (the returning current), it will be found that those above cancel those below.*

ing current has a frequency of 60 cycles to the hour instead of 60 to the second. In one minute on this new time scale the current will complete one cycle. Suppose we start off the current in circuit *AD* as the clock strikes the hour, at 20 seconds past start off the current in *BE,* and at 40 seconds past, the current in *CF.* We are still running three single-phase circuits each carrying 100 amperes, but note this extraordinary thing. If we bring wires *D, E,* and *F* together in contact with one another they will share their three currents and will have no current at all! Because their three currents are out of phase, they cancel one another. The magic of the experiment is that we can take away those three wires *D, E,* and *F* and the circuit continues to carry the load on wires *A, B,* and *C* alone. Engineers use three-phase current to transmit power over long distances because it saves copper.

How are the three currents started off one after another and maintained in that order so regularly? When the stator of the large generator is wound during manufacture, three separate sets of coils are arranged: one at the hour, one at the angle of 20 minutes past, and one at 40 minutes past. The large rotating magnet in the rotor sweeps past them in turn: first in one, then in the second, and followed by the third. In this way the separate circuits brought out from these three separate coils have their sine waves of current distributed as shown in the diagram. The same principle applies when the frequency is 60 cycles a second.

Up to the present the world's supply of electricity has been produced almost entirely from coal or water power. Today we are at the threshold of a completely new era. A wonderful development is taking place at a revolutionary pace. At a time when we are beginning to see the end of our coal resources in the face of vastly increased demands for electric power, scientists have discovered a new source of energy—atomic energy. Already a number of small power stations have been built and many others are being planned. Although the discoveries which have led to this movement are only a few years old, nuclear power may ultimately supersede all other known sources of energy.

Nuclear power, when applied to the supply of electricity, does not replace the present power station with its steam turbines, electric generators, transformers, and so on. What it does is to substitute a nuclear reactor for the usual boiler. There are many new accessories accompanying the reactor; and some of the items which at present are associated with the boiler, such as the coal-handling plant, disappear; but with nuclear power, steam is still used to drive turbogenerators.

There is much still to be learned about nuclear energy, but the main points are easily comprehended. In the first place certain substances are radioactive; that is, they throw out a continuous stream of tiny high-speed particles. Professor Rutherford, who did important research in the field of radioactivity, made this wonderful discovery at McGill University, in Canada, and Cambridge University, in England. He found that by using these particles as bullets he could release similar particles from other substances. Further discoveries followed and led to what is called the chain reaction. Then uranium came into the picture. A remarkable feature about uranium in its natural state is that, although it is one of the chemical elements, it consists of two distinct kinds of uranium. When elements can appear in two different forms, they are called *isotopes;* the two important isotopes of uranium are uranium 235 (U 235) and uranium 238 (U 238). The figures 235 and 238 represent the atomic number and there is usually very much more of the U 238 than of the U 235. There is a third isotope of uranium, U 234, but it occurs only in about one part in a thousand and is of little interest for our present purpose.

In natural uranium only one part in 140 is U 235. Now U 235 is *fissionable,* or capable of being split. When a neutron (a high-speed, high-energy particle) strikes one of the atomic nuclei of U 235, it produces additional neutrons which are then available to continue the process. Uranium 235 is the only fissionable element found in nature. Each additional nucleus can go on and produce more by further bombardment. This is known as a chain reaction. Unless the process is stopped in some way, it can get completely out of hand.

When a uranium 235 nucleus is made to undergo fission by the bombardment of a neutron, about two and a half new neutrons are produced. These flying particles are very penetrating and tend to escape; therefore some of the increase of two and a half times is lost. Some of the neutrons are captured by impurities in the surrounding substances and others are captured by the second part of the uranium, the U 238. Then this group produces an important change in the U 238; it converts the U 238 into another substance, *plutonium.* Although U 238 is not fissionable, plutonium is!

The small quantity of U 235 sends out neutrons to an increasing extent. Some escape, many convert U 238 into plutonium, and some are available to make a chain reaction.

The field of atomic energy has brought forth a number of new terms. A *breeder,* for example, is a reactor which ends up with more fissionable material than it started with. This comes about by the neutrons from the U 235 converting the U 238 into plutonium which itself can continue the work, although the U 238 could not. Such a reactor breeds nuclear fuel. Another term is *enriched uranium.* This is simply nuclear fuel consisting of U 235 and U 238; but, instead of the U 235 being only one part in 140, it is a much bigger proportion and therefore more effective.

If uranium or plutonium is used instead of coal in a power station, the reactor must bring pieces of the fuel together so that the chain reaction can start. It must have arrangements for controlling the reaction; otherwise, instead of a power station, we would have an atom bomb and, in a few minutes, complete disaster. Today we already know enough about the control methods necessary. They are well understood and safe so that there is no risk of a properly designed reactor's running away. The control is effected by using what is called a *moderator.* This is a slowing down material which captures the neutrons without fission.

The reactor must also provide some means of removing the heat generated and using it to produce steam for driving the generator sets. Since the radioactive materials produced in the reactor are very dangerous to human beings, thirdly, elaborate health precautions have to be taken in the design of the installation. The fourth main requirement is the provision which has to be made for removing the fuel from time to time for chemical processing and separation of fission products, a very costly operation.

Although there are many experimental reactors operating in different countries, the Calder Hall Station, in Britain, was the

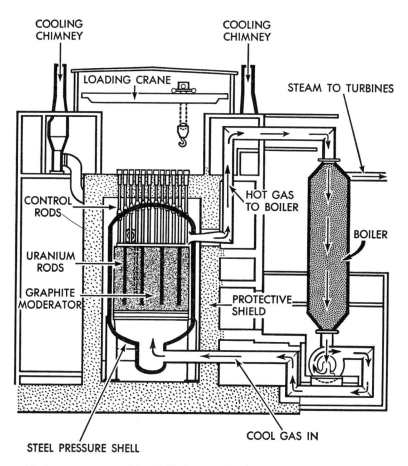

Nuclear reactor at Calder Hall, showing details of construction. (Adapted from The Economist)

first nuclear power station to provide electricity as a commercial proposition. Even this station was intended primarily to produce plutonium, and its electrical output of 50,000 kilowatts is modest compared with the expected output of other stations planned in the United States, Britain, and Russia.

In the Calder Hall reactor the moderator is a block of graphite, and the rods of active material are arranged to slide in and out as required. Carbon-dioxide gas under pressure is used for cooling, or transferring the heat to the boilers.

The choice between graphite-moderated piles cooled by gas blown through them and others using water for cooling depends on the location of the station. The use of a water-cooled pile is not quite so safe in operation as one which is gas cooled and therefore not so suitable for use in a populated area.

In the Calder Hall Station a mass of graphite, weighing 1000 tons, is built up of machined blocks with a number of vertical channels left in the block. In these channels rods of uranium fuel and boron steel for control can slide up and down, and they are raised and lowered by means of an electric crane spanning the top of the reactor. For emergency use a number of boron steel rods are suspended in such a way that, by the pressing of a button, they are released and caused to drop quickly into holes provided for them in the pile.

The pressure vessel is constructed of 2-inch welded steel plates and is about 40 feet in diameter and 60 feet high. It is charged with carbon dioxide and requires about 20 tons of the gas. Outside the pressure vessel is the concrete wall known as a *biological screen,* which prevents any dangerous radiation from reaching the personnel employed. When the gas has been heated in the reactor, it is passed through a heat exchanger 18 feet in diameter and 70 feet high, which transfers the heat from the gas through many 2-inch tubes and so produces the steam to operate the turbogenerators. There are two reactors, and the generator house is situated between them. There are four turbines, each capable of producing 23,000 kilowatts.

The Calder Hall Station may be described as an ordinary reactor. It uses natural uranium, and it is simple and safe. But the next few years will see the development of many types, slow and fast, using various materials.

In the stations of the future various modifications of the Calder Hall design will be introduced. Instead of graphite for the moderator, heavy water, ordinary water, beryllium, and other substances will be tried.

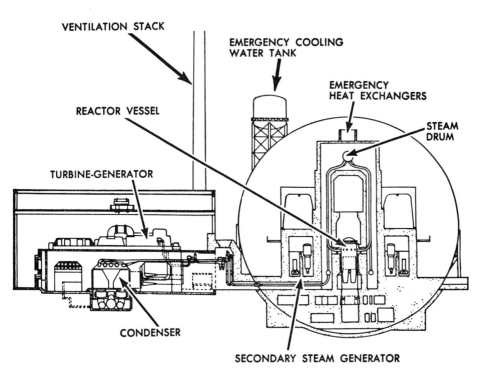

The Dresden Nuclear Power Station near Chicago, Ill. The steel sphere enclosing the reactor is 190 feet in diameter. (Adapted from General Electric Co.)

Instead of the express neutrons being slowed down, as is done in the ordinary thermal reactors, they will sometimes be used at their original high speed in what is called a *fast* reactor. In this type no moderator is used.

Atomic energy has brought about a real revolution in the production of electric power. Soon coal will cease to have the important place it holds at present and even the remarkable atomic developments of today may become quite commonplace. We are told that with a fast reactor we might be able to generate 100,000 kilowatts in a reactor coil no bigger than a garbage can.

An important part of many electric supply systems is the underground network of distribution cables. An electric cable may take one of many forms, but all types have certain features in common. Naturally the most important component is the conductor that carries the current but, to ensure that the current remains in the conductor all the way from the source to the lamp, motor, or other device where it is used, the conductor must be efficiently insulated. Without a suitable covering, short circuits and leaks would occur and, as a means of transmitting the current, the cable would be a failure.

In most types of cable there is also required, in addition to the conductor and insulation, some form of protection against external damage. These three parts of a cable—the conductor, the insulator, and the protection—are so varied for different types of cable that their design has become a problem in electrical engineering. Moreover, a wide range of materials is used and great ingenuity has been displayed in perfecting the machinery employed in their manufacture.

The size of the conductor depends on the magnitude of the current to be carried. It would be useless to try to supply a whole row of houses with current through a flexible cord such as that used for carrying a single bulb: the cord would burn out. So far as material is concerned, copper is by far the most popular. Silver, being a better conducting material than copper, could be used but the cost of this metal is too high. Notwithstanding the very great increase in prices which have occurred over the past few years, copper is still the metal most used for cable conductors, although aluminum is being used to an ever increasing extent.

Cables are made in long lengths and have to be transported on reels. Very often in use they must be bent around corners and threaded into ducts, so one very important property is flexibility. In any but the smallest conductors, therefore, a solid copper wire or rod is unsuitable—it is much too rigid. To construct a large copper conductor in such a way that it can be bent or wound on reels, a process called *stranding* is used. The copper is produced in the form of reasonably small wires and then these separate wires are twisted together.

A number of different processes are involved in producing the stranded conductor. Pure copper is first rolled down while hot into round rods a little less than half an inch in diameter. After being pickled in acid baths to remove the black scale, these rods are then pulled cold through a series of steel reducing dies which reduce the diameter gradually, until it is the size required. At this stage the wire is shiny but is so hard that it has to be annealed by heating again. This is done in special furnaces with the air kept way so that there is no tarnishing. Then the wire is ready for the stranding operation.

Stranding consists of taking a number of reels, each containing a long length of wire, and by means of a stranding machine rotating them around one another. If you draw on your paper a cross section of a stranded conductor consisting of separate round wires, you will see that there is a definite geometrical pattern. If you start with one wire in the center and then lay six wires the same size as the first around it, they just fill the circle. There is only one correct number, and that is six, which just

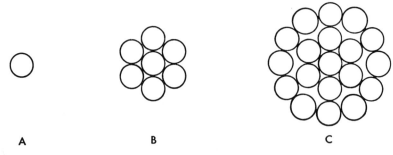

Construction of stranded cable conductors. (A) *Single wire.* (B) *A seven-strand conductor.* (C) *A nineteen-strand conductor.*

fit round the one. That is why so often we find a conductor called a seven-strand. If we proceed to a second layer, laid in the opposite direction so as to hold everything together, we require just twelve more. And so on. In the illustration opposite the individual bobbins, each carrying a length of one wire, are supported on rotating cages. The wires are collected together at a die to form the finished conductor which is coiled up on the final reel ready for the next operation.

A modern high-speed stranding machine has the individual reels along the center of a hollow cylinder which rotates around them, picks off the wires, and passes them out to the die where they emerge as the complete stranded conductor.

The two principal forms of insulation applied to the stranded conductor are, on the one hand, a tape of paper or woven fibrous material and, on the other, rubberlike material applied as a continuous coating. In smaller cables, such as those used for wiring buildings, rubber or plastic insulation is general. In order to provide a lasting coating which will not deteriorate with age, the basic rubber is compounded with various other ingredients. These substances in powder and liquid form are incorporated in large mixing machines which produce a plastic dough. This is then applied to the conductor either as a thin sheet or extruded as a tube, usually the latter. In the sheet method, more general abroad than in the United States and rapidly disappearing, a number of conductors are passed side by side between a pair of steel rolls with strips of the insulating sheet above and below the wires. The rolls press the material down onto the wires which emerge completely coated and, separating themselves from one another, go on to separate reels.

In the more usual extrusion process the dough or plastic is fed into the hopper of a machine like a sausage machine. Here an internal rotating screw takes hold of the material and forces it out through a die surrounding the wire or stranded conductor to be covered.

When synthetic plastic materials are used, no further process

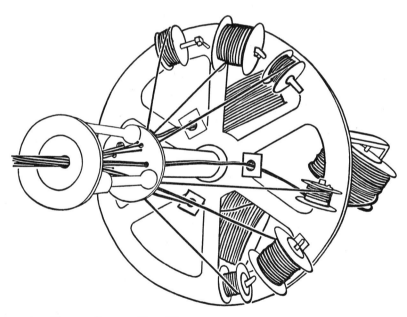

A cable-stranding machine. The separate components of the cable are assembled in bobbins on the large cage. As this rotates, the conductors and packings leave the bobbins, move to the left and are assembled through a steel die into the built-up cable.

is necessary, but with rubber products a process called *vulcanization* follows. This hardens the soft coating and gives it enduring properties. This process is carried out on large autoclaves, or ovens, in which the reels of cable are heated by steam under pressure.

Most cables for transmission and distribution of electricity under our city streets are insulated with paper that is impregnated with an oily compound. Paper strip about an inch or less in width is wrapped by a lapping machine around the conductor in the form of a continuous spiral. Many layers are applied until the necessary thickness has been attained and then the whole is subjected to a drying and impregnating process.

Moisture is fatal to this type of cable so it is always covered with a continuous waterproof sheath, usually of lead. The method

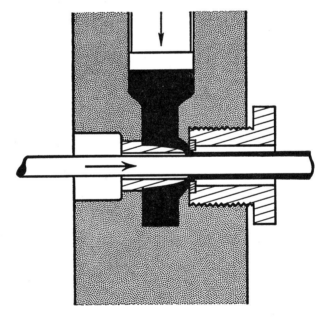

Hydraulic cable-sheathing press. As the cable passes horizontally through the die box of the press, hot lead is forced around it by hydraulic pressure and forms a continuous tube.

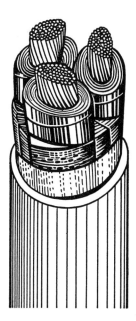

Telescoped sample of three-core insulated underground cable. The three separate cores are laid up—that is, twisted around one another—and the assembly incased in a lead sheath.

of applying this sheath is of interest and very important, as the least pinhole in the lead might admit moisture and cause the cable to fail. The lead, while hot, is squeezed around the cable by a hydraulic cylinder which gives a force of many tons. The plastic metal passes through steel dies, and both cable and lead tube move forward from the press as a continuous whole.

When a double-wire circuit is required, it is usual to place the "go" and "return" conductors inside one common lead tube. For three-phase circuits the three conductors are placed inside the one tube and form a single cable. For economy, to keep the diameter of the cable to a minimum, the stranded conductors are often squeezed into a *D* shape, or sector shape, as shown in the illustration. In multicore cables the component cores are twisted together, or laid up, by a laying-up machine in which separate reels carrying the component insulated conductors are rotated around one another. The cores emerge through a die and are then held together by a tape wrapped around them.

In Europe large quantities of power cables are buried directly in the ground and, to protect the lead sheath of such cables, an armoring of steel wire or tape is applied. In the United States such cable, often known as Parkway cable, is used to a lesser extent; but the general practice is to draw power cables into underground conduits provided for the purpose. Fiber, tile, or concrete ducts are assembled in a trench in the ground with a small space between them which is filled with concrete so that ultimately they provide a solid block of concrete with continuous holes. At convenient intervals, say five hundred to a thousand feet, manholes are provided and, when the cables of limited length are drawn into the conduits, they can be jointed together. Manholes also provide facilities for diverting circuits and for giving access to the cables without disturbing the surface of the road.

Junctions between sections of cable are connected, after laying, by means of splices to form a continuous circuit. Splices are also made to lead off branch circuits from main feeders. For this purpose lead sleeves or cast-iron boxes form the protective covering between the two ends of cable. The conductors are joined together by a brass ferrule, and insulating tapes are applied over this to make the insulation continuous. In many cases the boxes are filled with a hot compound which solidifies on cooling and prevents ingress of moisture. To terminate a cable, special terminal boxes are provided, some of quite complex design, to give facilities for disconnecting or inserting fuses in the circuit.

CHAPTER **10**

Telecommunications

THE whole field of electrical engineering is conveniently divided into two distinct parts—heavy current and light current. Instead of discussing hundreds of thousands of amperes that are used in power supply, we shall now deal with tiny currents of milliamperes (thousandths of an ampere), and our conductors for carrying the current will not be massive bars and strands of copper or aluminum but quite small wires.

A major part of light-current engineering is that which embraces telecommunications (*tele* is Greek for "distance"). It comprises the telegraph (writing at a distance), telephone (talking at a distance), and television (seeing at a distance).

When two people talk to one another in the same room, the speaker by means of his voice mechanism produces sound waves. These travel through the air and impinge on the eardrum of the listener where, through a curious and rather wonderful mechanism, they cause messages to reach the brain. The telephone does not take the place of the speaker's larynx or of the listener's ear. What it does is to convert the speech of the speaker into electrical waves, pass them along a wire and, at the receiving end, convert the electrical current back into sound waves.

Imagine yourself blowing down a tube which is closed at the far end by an elastic diaphragm. When you exhale, the diaphragm

189

bulges out. Inhale and it bulges in. If you exhale and inhale repeatedly, you will be sending waves along the air in the tube; the movement of the diaphragm will be the mechanism receiving the unseen waves and converting them into movement.

Sound waves cannot be seen, but there are many phenomena which prove the existence of sound waves. For example, a jet plane roars overhead and it has gone before you hear it. The sound waves which it produces take time to travel through the air from the plane to the ear and by that time the jet has moved a mile or more. A quickly approaching locomotive blows its whistle as it passes you standing by the track. The note emitted suddenly drops. While approaching you, the whistle is catching up on the sound waves it is making, so crowding them together and giving your ear more waves to the second—a higher pitch —than if it were stationary. As the train leaves you, the waves are stretched out, made longer, so that fewer reach you per second. The pitch is lower.

Waves in themselves are interesting—water waves, sound waves, light waves, and so on. If you stand on a breakwater, you will notice that an incoming wave is reflected and travels out again. In so doing it often meets another incoming wave and suddenly there is no traveling wave at all but just a lumping up and down. This is called a stationary wave. Light waves go straight; you cannot see around the corner of the street, but you can hear the brass band in the next street because sound waves do go around corners. We hang a watch in a glass bell jar and can just hear it ticking; when we pump the air out of the jar, the sound disappears. There is no air to transmit the waves.

The problem to be solved by the telephone is to convert the sound waves produced by the speaker into electric current at one place and reconvert into sound waves at another place—possibly thousands of miles away. We must produce in a circuit electric waves of the same shape and pitch as the sound waves. We can

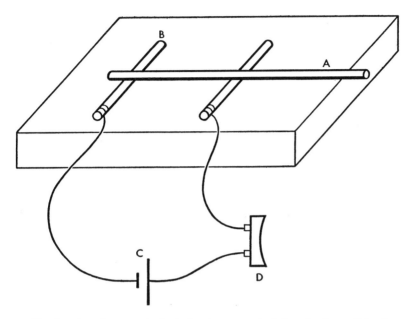

Simple microphone made by balancing a two-inch length of pencil lead (A) so that it lightly touches a second piece (B) on a sounding board, an empty small box. Such an arrangement with a battery (C) and simple receiver (D) will transmit speech some distance.

then obtain, at the far end, an exact reproduction of our friend's voice.

The instrument used to convert sound waves into waves of electric current is called a *microphone*. There are various forms of microphones, but the one that is by far the most generally used varies the resistance of the current according to the pressure of air waves and so varies the current in the circuit. This is done by enclosing a quantity of carbon granules in a small chamber between two plates of metal or carbon. One of the plates is fixed and the other is attached to a diaphragm on which the sound waves impinge. When the diaphragm is pushed in by the air wave, the granules are compressed and make a better contact with one another. When the pressure wave passes, the diaphragm springs out again and releases the compression of the granules. In this way the electrical resistance of the mass of granules changes rapidly with the movement of the diaphragm, and the current in the circuit connected to the two electrodes, or plates, gives a faithful reproduction of the sound wave.

The drawing shows a carbon-granule microphone transmitter in section. The speaker talks into the perforated disk on the left and the sound waves strike the conical plate, or diaphragm, which presses against the carbon granules in the center. The current travels from the spring contact in the center, through the carbon granules, to the outer rim and the spring contact. The conical plate is made of springy metal and can be rigidly supported around its circumference, but the center is sufficiently flexible for the pressure of the sound waves to cause the electrode

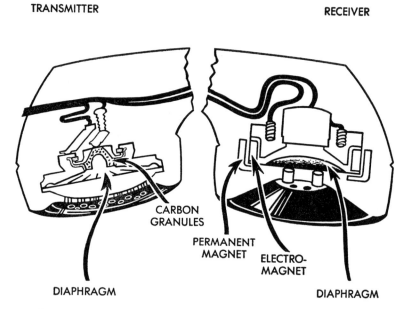

TRANSMITTER

RECEIVER

CARBON GRANULES

PERMANENT MAGNET

ELECTRO-MAGNET

DIAPHRAGM

DIAPHRAGM

Telephone handset, showing transmitter and receiver in section. (Adapted from American Telephone and Telegraph Co.)

to move backward and forward. In the practical instrument a molded plastic mouthpiece is usually fitted as part of the supporting handset.

With the sound waves at the transmitter converted into electric current waves, it next becomes necessary to reconvert the electric current waves into sound waves at the receiver. This is done by a piece of equipment as ingenious and as simple as the microphone. The receiver, again about the size of a large thick watch, has a circular case which holds by its outer edge a thin diaphragm of magnetic material. Placed close to the diaphragm is an electromagnet with its poles only a fraction of an inch away so that a current in the coils of the magnet causes the diaphragm to be attracted. The extent of the attraction depends on the value of the current and the movement of the diaphragm is an exact reproduction of the changing current in the magnet coils. The diaphragm, as soon as it moves, presses on the air in contact with it and so produces sound waves which in turn vary as the current. If this current comes from a speech-operated microphone in the same circuit, the sound waves given out from the magnetic diaphragm reproduce the original speech.

The sectional diagram shows the practical construction of a modern telephone receiver. The disk of magnetic material, usually an alloy with better properties than ordinary soft iron, is shown in section as a straight line and the two pole pieces of the electromagnet, each provided with surrounding coils of wire, stand close to the disk. The receiver would operate with the magnetic field produced by the received currents alone; but, to increase its effectiveness, a permanent magnet is added. This connects the two electromagnets behind the coils and so provides a continuous attraction on the disk whether or not speech currents are being received. The speech currents strengthen or weaken this attraction of the permanent magnet, and all of the time the moving disk is held under control by the permanent magnet. A great deal of research has been carried out on the different magnetic metals to be used for the disk, the permanent magnet, and the pole pieces because they all have different characteristics. By the addition of such metals as aluminum and nickel to the iron we have arrived at the very highly efficient instrument to which we are now accustomed.

Before we turn from microphones and receivers, a word should perhaps be said about the types of instruments which are constructed for specific purposes. For broadcasting and public address systems, for instance, there are special requirements: these microphones do not employ the granule principle. In one of these the speech currents are generated in a moving coil carried by the diaphragm near a powerful permanent magnet. The currents are generated by changes of magnetic field in the coil as they are in the ordinary dynamo—by electromagnetic induction. Of less general importance is the condenser microphone in which two plates forming an electric condenser are moved backward and forward by the speech waves. This type has advantages when pure speech is required for recording purposes and in laboratory work. In this case, lack of distortion over the whole frequency range is more important than high sensitivity. When speech volume must be heightened on a loudspeaker without a lot of complication in the use of amplifiers, as for instance on a police car, a carbon-granule microphone with more than one pair of electrodes is used.

Alternative types of receivers are also used in which the moving-coil principle is adopted, although this is not often used for ordinary telephone circuits.

The microphone and receiver must be combined to make an instrument convenient for everyday use. In the popular handset which we pick up when the bell rings, the microphone and receiver are combined. In other and older forms of instruments the microphone is carried on a pedestal or on a wall box and the receiver is held separately. In all cases there are circuit arrangements for combining the bell with the speech components.

The bell is usually operated by alternating current specially generated for the purpose. It is known as a *magneto* bell. There are two coils forming a two-pole electromagnet and an armature is pivoted opposite the pole pieces and connected to an arm with a hammer which strikes between two gongs. A permanent magnet, called a *polarizing* magnet, induces polarity in the soft-iron armature, which is attracted first to one pole of the electromagnet and then to the other as the current alternates.

When a telephone installation consists simply of two stations working from one to the other, each station requires a magneto-generator for calling the other and a battery to be cut in to provide the necessary current for transmitting the speech. This change is usually effected by a switch, which comes into operation when the person wishing to speak lifts the receiver.

The more usual arrangement in towns is to concentrate the battery at the central exchange and to send out the speaking current when the subscriber lifts his receiver. By the same operation the current works the calling signal at the exchange. In this

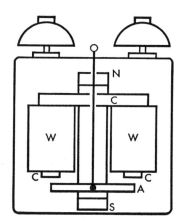

Magneto bell. (C) *Soft iron core of electromagnet.* (A) *Armature fixed to bell hammer.* (W) *Magnet windings supplied with alternating current.* (N, S) *Permanent polarizing magnet.*

central battery system magneto bells are used at the subscriber's instrument and are operated by large magneto generators in the exchange through the operator's key. There is no longer any cranking of magnetos by the subscriber to call the exchange. The illustration on page 197 shows this type of arrangement.

To call the exchange we lift our receiver. A current from the central battery flows in from one exchange line through our transmitter and through one of the contacts on the receiver switch and then out on the other line. At the exchange this current operates a calling device which lights a lamp. When we have been connected to the required subscriber, the speaking circuit is completed between the two stations by switches in the exchange. Calls from the exchange are signaled by the use of alternating current produced by a magneto. This current has no difficulty in passing through condenser E and the coils of bell A, whereas the direct current for speaking and signaling the exchange can flow only through a metallic circuit.

When we talk into the transmitter (B), the fluctuating current so generated passes through the transformer (D) and out to the exchange line. At the same time, this fluctuating current passes through a circuit composed of the receiver (C), the inner winding of the transformer, and the condenser (E), which it can do since it is, in effect, an alternating current. This current induces a higher voltage in the outer winding of the transformer and boosts the voice-carrying current. This, in outline, is the principle of central battery working. Owing to the introduction of many refinements, circuit diagrams have become much more complicated and only the rudimentary principles can be illustrated here.

Until recent years most telephone exchanges were manually operated. The operator sat in front of a board with a number of holes, in each of which the line of one particular subscriber was terminated. While manual operation has almost entirely disap-

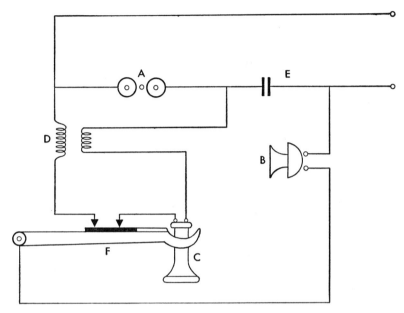

Simple telephone circuit, connected to exchange having a magneto and battery. (A) Bell. (B) Transmitter. (C) Receiver. (D) Transformer. (E) Condenser. (F) Switch arm. Lines to exchange are at upper right.

peared in the United States in favor of automatic working, there are many exchanges in other countries on the manual system.

On the board opposite the operator there were rows of *jacks*, or holes, and adjacent to each one was a tiny bulb which lit up when the connected subscriber lifted his receiver. On the bench in front of the operator were a number of plugs which could be inserted into these holes and which were connected to the operator's headphone. When she saw a signal light up, she inserted a plug called the *answering* plug and was at once in contact with that subscriber. After ascertaining what number he required, she then took a second plug connected with the first as a pair—this one called a *calling* plug—and, searching among a number of holes for the one with the number being called, she inserted the plug, thus connecting the two subscribers together.

This was not quite as simple an operation as it seems. In the first place every operator on the switchboard could plug into this same required subscriber. There were many thousand on one exchange and the lines were repeated around the board to make them available to the different operators. Thus two operators could connect the same required subscriber to two calling subscribers, but a simple device prevented this from happening. There was a metal ring around the hole of the jack and, when the subscriber was connected, all the rings in the other positions were automatically made alive. The result was that when a second operator attempted to take that particular line for a second caller she received a tiny "click" in her headphone, indicating that the line was busy.

The second complication which had to be provided for when the calling plug was inserted in the required subscriber's jack was that he must be called. It was not sufficient to connect him to the friend who wanted to talk. He did not know and did not lift his receiver even if the line was complete. Consequently a ringing key was provided for each calling plug and by pressing this for a second the operator sent out an alternating current from the magneto ringer in the exchange which rang the bell of the wanted subscriber. Consequently he lifted his receiver and then the speaking current was completed and conversation could proceed. When the conversation was through and the subscribers hung up their receivers, more lamps lit up on the switchboard to indicate to the operator that she could withdraw the two plugs.

In modern telephone systems the subscriber is provided with a dialing instrument by which he spells out the number of the person he wishes to be connected to. Within a few seconds the apparatus in the exchange, quite automatically and without any human aid, searches out from among the thousands of lines connected to the exchange the one required, applies the ringing current, and then connects the two together. Much ingenuity

has been displayed in the design of the various pieces of equipment employed and an automatic exchange is a complicated thing.

We will start with a very simple exchange of ten subscribers.
If we can first of all make a simple switch with an arm sliding
over nine contacts and connect these contacts with the lines of
the other nine subscribers, all we require is some means of working this switch from a distance. The iron core of an electromagnet
always attracts a nearby armature when the current flows. This
principle is applied extensively in telephone exchanges through
a device called a *relay*. If the armature of a relay is provided
with contacts, it can be used for connecting up a further circuit
through the operation of the current in the main circuit, and this
is the usual method of employing a relay; one current coming
from a distance starts and stops another current, generally a
local one.

The relay has another practical application. The movement of
the armature, instead of closing electrical contacts, operates a
mechanism of the ratchet and pawl variety so well known in
clockwork trains. The diagram shows such a relay with a pawl

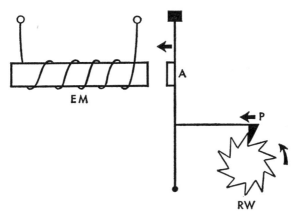

Ratchet and pawl mechanism used in automatic telephone equipment.
(EM) Electromagnet. (A) Armature. (RW) Ratchet wheel. (P) Pawl.
Pulled to left when armature A is attracted by electromagnet EM.

fixed to the armature. The pawl engages the teeth of a ratchet wheel so that, every time the current is applied, the wheel is rotated by one tooth. When the current stops, the pawl slips back ready to pull on the next tooth. If now we fix a metal arm to the spindle of the ratchet wheel and arrange for the end of the arm to slide over nine contacts, we only need connect the telephone lines from our nine friends to these nine contacts and we can connect any one at will. We have advanced the first stage to an automatic telephone exchange. If we want to talk to subscriber No. 7, we send a current seven times to the relay and No. 7 will be connected immediately.

In practice it would be irksome to have to count how many current impulses were sent to the exchange so a simple device has been invented to do the counting for us. On the telephone instrument is a dial with a number of holes which are numbered 1 to 9, and then 0. The dial can be pulled around by the finger against a spring and on the spindle inside the case is a metal disk with notches on it, each notch corresponding to a number. Associated with the disk is a pawl connected to electrical contacts so that when we put our finger in the hole marked 7 and pull it around and then release it, the spring pulls it back again. The pawl passes over 7 notches and gives 7 clicks to the electrical contact which sends the required 7 impulses to the exchange to work our automatic switch there.

Now if that were all there is to it an automatic exchange might be a very simple thing, but imagine the complexities that arise when you want to select one line from 10,000 instead of 10. Think of the precautions which must be taken to select, ring, and speak in turn, all on one pair of wires from you to the exchange. Imagine the vast array of relays required. Consider also the confusion that could occur if all the thousands of connections were not kept separate from one another. To call a subscriber—say number 73 on a 100-line exchange—first we dial 7, then 3.

In the exchange the first number dialed operates a tens mechanism and the second number a unit mechanism as before. All the problems are solved by breaking them down into simpler problems.

The kernel of the system is a device called a *two-motion* selector which consists of a semicircular assembly of contacts, 100 in all, arranged in 10 tiers with 10 contacts in each tier. In the middle of the assembly is a vertical spindle, carrying a contact arm which, by rotation, can make contact with 10 different fixed contacts in one tier. It can also be raised or lowered to bring its ends in line with the different tiers of fixed contacts. By moving up and down and sideways the moving arm can connect to any one of 100 lines.

The working of the two-motion selector is controlled by two relays: one that rotates the arm and one that raises and lowers the arm. On the spindle there are two ratchets. The vertical one enables the pawl of one of the relays to lift the spindle 1, 2, 3, or more teeth up to 10, depending on the number of impulses received. The horizontal one having teeth along the spindle enables the pawl of the other relay in the same way to rotate the spindle and arm round 1, 2, 3, or more positions. At this stage, then, operating the dial to send the number 73 first steps up the spindle of the two-motion selector to the seventh vertical position, and rotates the spindle to the third contact on the horizontal seventh tier. By sending the correct number of impulses from the instrument we can secure connection with any one of the 100 other subscribers connected to this two-motion selector.

In large exchanges where we wish to select a subscriber with, say, a four-figure number, as 5673, we need several of these selectors and a principle is used whereby the apparatus automatically searches for free or disengaged paths. This principle is best understood by a reference to what happens when we first lift our receiver. Before we start to dial a number we wait for the dial tone, a well-recognized buzz in the receiver. If we attempt to dial before we receive the dial tone we get nowhere. Automatic telephone exchanges are designed on the assumption that only a small proportion of the connected subscribers ring at the same time. This permits a considerable economy in the provision of line-selecting mechanism.

Of course if only one selector is provided for every ten connected subscribers, each must be able to obtain the selector when he wants it and this is provided for by having a device known as a *uniselector* connected to every line. As soon as we lift our receiver our own uniselector in the exchange goes hunting for a selector not in use. It does this by means of a rotating wiper arm which moves over contact after contact. If it comes to a contact already in use it automatically moves on to another. As soon as it finds one not in use it comes to rest and sends us the news by means of the dial tone. We are now connected to a final selector and can send our impulses, which rotate the dial and so, step by step, start the subsequent two-motion switches going through the process of choosing the thousands, then the hundreds, followed by the tens and the digits of the number required. As quickly as our dial returns each time after we have moved it for the individual figures, so do these switches follow up step by step; and when the process is complete they connect the ringing current to the desired line and connect us through. Once their work is completed for this occasion the selectors drop out of the circuit and become available for carrying out the same performance for other subscribers.

The transmission of speech currents from place to place calls for a special type of electric cable and indeed for very stringent precautions. One cable must carry many circuits all insulated from one another. There may be as many as 1,000 pairs of wires under one lead sheath and every pair provides the "go" and "return" for one conversation. There is a risk of magnetic flux caused by the current in one pair linking with another pair and generating a current in the second pair. Since the first current is a speech current and fluctuates with the voice of the speaker, any such induction will cause the speech to be transferred to the second wire. This is called *overhearing* and special precautions must be taken to prevent it.

The same phenomenon occurs in bare telephone wires on pole lines. The steps taken to avoid overhearing are perhaps best explained in the overhead wire circuit. Suppose two wires, *A* and *B*, run alongside two other wires, *C* and *D*, for some miles. Although they are completely insulated from one another by their porcelain or glass supports, there will be sufficient magnetic leakage passing from the *AB* circuit to the *CD* circuit to cause overhearing. The remedy adopted is very simple. Halfway along the line a cross is put into one of the circuits. Suppose the cross is made on the *CD* circuit; for half the total distance along the line the influence of the magnetic induction on the *AB* circuit by the *CD* circuit is one way around, but in the second half it is the opposite way around. Thus the overhearing is completely eliminated.

In a cable the effect of crossing over the wires on different pairs is obtained by twisting the individual pairs during manu-

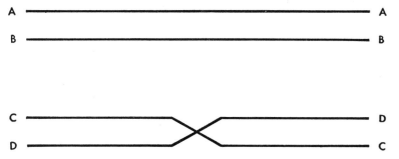

Prevention of overhearing between adjacent telephone circuits by the insertion of crosses in the wires.

facture with various pitches; for instance, if the wires of pair *AB* are twisted around one another every twelve inches and the wires of pair *CD* around one another every six inches, the effect is the same as putting a crossover in *CD* halfway along the open line in the previous example.

Another important characteristic of telephone cables is the capacitance between wires. In chapter 1 we saw that a charge on one conductor induced a charge on a nearby conductor, as in the Leyden jar or the electrophorus. This is known as a condenser. In a telephone cable the two wires of a pair form such a condenser. They run close together for miles. When the speech currents from our microphone enter such a circuit, their first effect is to charge this condenser; and more and more of the current at the sending end becomes locked up in charging the wires, leaving less and less to come out at the far end to convey the speech to the listener.

For this reason, in the design and manufacture of telephone cables, very special care is taken to keep the electrostatic capacity between wires as small as possible, done by employing the air-spaced paper insulated construction. A condenser with air between the metal plates has a lower capacitance than one with solid substance, but at the same time some solid separator is necessary to prevent the wires from coming into contact with one another. The usual way of getting out of this dilemma is to wrap each of the conductors very loosely with a paper strip held on by a thread of cotton spiraled around it. This produces a ballooning of the paper which acts as an effective separator with a large air content. When many circuits of this kind are assembled, the cable is dried in ovens and a lead sheath is applied, providing a protection against any ingress of moisture.

In long-distance telephone cables not only does the electromagnetic interference between one pair and another have to be balanced to prevent overhearing, but also the effect of differences in electrostatic capacitance must be balanced. Most elaborate precautions are taken in testing and joining the wires in one length of cable with those in the next. It is a remarkable thing that with hundreds of wires all lying closely together for many miles in one lead tube, this balancing is carried out so effectively that we have complete silence on our own telephone line except for the one subscriber we are speaking with.

When telephone circuits get longer than a few miles—and many are thousands of miles long—new problems arise; among them are *distortion* and *attenuation*. When a radio is badly tuned, the voice of the speaker comes through with an unnatural squeak or in low gruff tones. This is due to distortion. The very nature of speech depends on complex sound waves, and changing the shape of the wave changes the nature of the sound. So it is in a telephone circuit. Suppose for some reason or other we take away that part of the wave which represents the high pitch, or the high-frequency element; immediately a woman's voice begins to sound like a man's. Even less distortion of the current wave will disguise the voice of our best friend.

Distortion in a telephone cable can be overcome by adding at intervals along a line what are called *loading coils*. These are coils of wire on special magnetic cores housed in iron pots which can be seen at intervals along a long-distance telephone cable carried on poles. One iron pot holds many such coils and each of the coils is connected in one of the circuits.

The second complexity is attenuation. As speech currents start off and travel down a long line, they become attenuated, or weakened, and as a result the speaker sounds as though he were a long way off. This is not a very important effect until we reach distances of many miles, but in all long-distance circuits it is now necessary to strengthen the current. Nothing can be done by pushing more energy into the speaking end; the weak speech, reaching a certain point, must be boosted up and helped on its way. This is done by a device known as a *repeater*. In the same way that a weak radio signal is received in a radio set and by means of electronic tubes boosted up to give us an audible signal, so the current weakened by traveling through miles of telephone cable is boosted up and sent on its way again.

As the requirements for more and more simultaneous conversations have increased, a new principle has been introduced to reduce the number of wires required. This is called *carrier telephony*. It enables several conversations to be carried on one pair of wires at the same time without interference with one another. The principle is very much the same as that used in radio speech, referred to as "wired radio."

In carrier telephony the current transmitted has a very high frequency, many times higher than that of voice waves. Instead of varying about 100 to a thousand or so, frequencies of many thousands per second are employed and the speech current which we wish to transmit is made to *modulate* the high-frequency carrier current. It is as if, instead of sending a direct current from a battery through our transmitting microphone, the microphone is fed with a high-frequency current. If the current used is reversed in direction, say, 10,000 times a second, the microphone does not respond to this high frequency and just continues to compress the carbon grains as the voice waves fall on it. The shape of the voice wave is thus transmitted to the distant end of the line.

Now suppose we take a second microphone and feed it with an alternating current which reverses in direction 20,000 times a second. This one can take a second conversation and both conversations can go down the same wire. The problem of separating the two conversations at the receiving end then arises, but this is easy to solve. Two tuned circuits are provided; one circuit is tuned to 10,000 cycles per second and the other to 20,000 cycles per second; in this way the two conversations can continue along the same pair of wires simultaneously. One pair of speakers knows nothing of the conversation of the other pair. Thus hundreds of conversations can be carried over one pair of wires.

Very high-frequency currents tend to interfere with adjacent circuits more than do ordinary speech frequencies, so the introduction of carrier telephony on cables has made the need for careful balancing much more important. The result in the long run has been the introduction of a new type of cable called the *coaxial* cable. In the coaxial cable there is only one pair of conductors. They are not twisted around one another, but one of the conductors is a copper tube and the other is a wire suspended along its center. Apart from the minimum amount of mechanical separation there is as much air space between the two as possible. As the inner conductor is completely screened from all external electrical interference by the outer conductor, the usual balance problems at very high frequency are overcome.

When a wire carries a very high-frequency current, the current does not distribute itself over the cross section of the conductor but crowds into the outside surface. It is as though the separate parts of the current were all pushing away from one another. This phenomenon is called the *skin effect*. In the coaxial cable the consequence of this skin effect is that the current passing outward by the inner wire and back by the outer tube crowds into the outer skin of the wire and the inner skin of the tube. Any effect from outside only affects the skin of the tube and so does not influence the actual circuit carrying the conversations on its inner skin.

The first coaxial cable was laid between New York and Philadelphia, but today there are thousands of miles in use all over the country and indeed all over the world, both for telephone purposes and for transmitting television programs.

The most remarkable and up-to-date advance in the telephone field is the telephone cable laid across the North Atlantic between

Britain and Newfoundland. It is a marvel of electrical ingenuity and embodies many of the most interesting applications of modern electrical science.

The story of the submarine cable starts with the early days of the electric telegraph. Prominent among the pioneers in this field was Professor Wheatstone of King's College, London, whose Wheatstone bridge is famous in electrical history. In the year 1837 Wheatstone was approached by W. F. Cooke who had become interested in the use of electricity for signaling at a distance. They formed a partnership and in a very short time Cooke and Wheatstone produced a telegraph system which was of commercial value. The first really practical installation was between London and Slough, on the Great Western Railway. The messages were sent by intermittent current which caused deflection of vertical magnetic needles according to an agreed code. This was a great achievement and people paid a shilling each to see the working of the instruments at the Paddington railway station.

There is a story told about this early telegraph. A woman was murdered in Slough and the suspected murderer was known by the police to have gone by train to London. A few years earlier he would have escaped, but the new telegraph was his undoing. A telegram was sent so that the murderer could be arrested on alighting from the train. The message read "He is in the garb of a Quaker." But there was no letter "Q" in the code alphabet so the operator spelled it "kwaker." This was misunderstood at first but, after some confusion and repetition, the description was transmitted to the police. The man was shadowed by a detective and ultimately arrested. The trial brought to light a remarkable career of vice, and the story which ended in the murderer's execution was a nationwide thriller. This sensational episode established the value of the telegraph for quick communication, and extensions rapidly followed.

A valuable contribution to the development of the telegraph

The Morse code.

A · –	J · – – –	S · · ·
B – · · ·	K – · –	T –
C – · – ·	L · – · ·	U · · –
D – · ·	M – –	V · · · –
E ·	N – ·	W · – –
F · · – ·	O – – –	X – · · –
G – – ·	P · – – ·	Y – · – –
H · · · ·	Q – – · –	Z – – · ·
I · ·	R · – ·	

was made in the United States by Samuel Morse, an artist and later professor of natural science at Yale University. In 1843 Morse invented the famous Morse code, consisting of combinations of dots and dashes to represent the different letters of the alphabet. This was quickly adopted and has been employed almost universally in telegraph signaling for over a century.

Morse also invented the key and sounder which bear his name. When the key is pressed down, a front contact on the pivoted arm touches a fixed contact on the base, connecting the center pivot to the base contact. In the normal position a spring on the back of the key keeps the lever in contact with a second fixed contact. Pressing the key and releasing it sends out short or long signals as required, known as dots and dashes, at the will of the operator. At the receiving end the current passes through the coils of an electromagnet in the sounder. Fixed to a pivoted arm

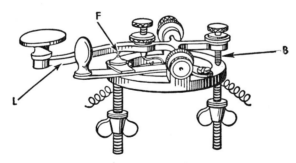

Morse telegraph key. (L) *Lever.* (B) *Back stop.* (F) *Front stop.*

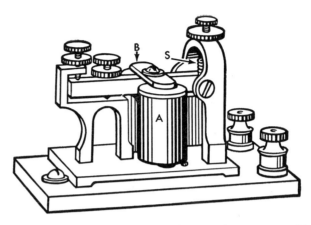

Morse sounder for receiving code signals. (A) *Electromagnet.* (B) *Soft iron armature.* (S) *Spring which holds lever against upper stop when no current is flowing in coil.*

is a soft iron bar which is attracted by the magnet while the current flows; when the current stops, a spring pulls up the bar against an upper stop. The message in Morse code is read by listening to the clicks as the lever of the sounder hammers on the upper and lower stops. By a simple circuit arrangement using the back stop of the key, received signals on the sounder are kept separate from those sent out by the key. Today keys and sounders are being replaced by automatic equipment.

In the early telegraph a vertical magnetic needle oscillated from side to side, depending on the direction of the current received. For a dot the current flowed in such a direction as to deflect the needle to the left, for a dash it moved to the right.

As the inland telegraphs developed, the idea of extending the service overseas soon became the subject of discussion, and it is not surprising, in view of the work of the pioneers, that the question of a cable from England to France was soon under consideration. The big problem to be faced was the insulation of the conductor. In a submarine cable subjected to great water pressure the slightest defect in the coating of the insulation will bring complete failure, so the question was to find a suitable substance for the purpose. Rubber was tried but found to have certain weaknesses. About this time a new substance, *gutta-percha,* somewhat resembling rubber, came to light. Gutta-percha is extracted from certain trees in Malay and, although chemically it resembles rubber, it differs in that it softens in hot water. It was soon found to have excellent insulating properties and, as it became plastic when heated, it could conveniently be applied to the conductor. During the past century thousands of miles of gutta-percha insulated submarine cables have been laid in all parts of the world, and it is only in recent years that its position has been challenged by new synthetic insulating materials.

The first major enterprise in the submarine-cable field was the achievement of two Englishmen, Jacob and John Brett. Between them they were able to muster the engineering knowledge and financial resources to launch a scheme for crossing the Strait of Dover. They formed a company, had twenty-five nautical miles of simple cable made by the Gutta-Percha Company, and laid it out across the Channel from a large reel seven feet in diameter and fifteen feet long on the deck of a steam tug, the *Goliah.*

The cable consisted simply of a single copper wire of No. 14 gage covered with gutta-percha to a diameter of half an inch. It was manufactured in hundred-yard lengths and these were then joined together, making a total weight of cable of five tons. No mechanical protection was provided outside the gutta-percha.

A few signals were transmitted through the cable across the English Channel, but unfortunately a French fisherman by a stroke of bad luck hooked up the cable with his anchor and cut out a piece as a curiosity. He thought he had caught a new kind of fish. But this did not deter the Bretts. They proceeded with a scheme to lay a second cable, this time of an improved type. A layer of hemp yarn was laid over the gutta-percha and a protective layer of galvanized-iron armoring wire was added over all. After many setbacks the cable was completed and laid in 1851 and proved entirely satisfactory. Ten years later it was continuing to render service, and the era of submarine cables was established.

Although lengths of submarine cable were laid in different parts of the world, it was not until 1856 that the major enterprise of a transatlantic cable was launched. A wealthy American, Cyrus W. Field, formed a company in association with others on both sides of the Atlantic and appointed a number of experts, some of whom are still well-known names in the field of electrical science.

This time a stranded conductor was used and the size was defined by its weight, a method long followed in submarine practice. It was 107 pounds per nautical mile. The gutta-percha was applied in three coats to reduce the risk of weak places and hemp yarn was added, together with eighteen seven-wire strands of No. 22 gage iron wire. All this brought the diameter of the cable to only about five-eighths inch. We now know how unsuitable this design was for deep-sea laying, and it is not surprising that failure followed. As there was no ship existing which could take the whole length of cable it was divided between two, *H.M.S. Agamemnon*, lent by the British government, and the U.S. frigate *Niagara*.

The *Niagara* encountered trouble within a few miles when the cable broke in the paying-out machinery. After it was spliced and payed out for three days the signals failed mysteriously for several hours. Then again the cable broke at a point where the depth was over two thousand fathoms and the expedition had to be abandoned for a year.

In 1858 a further attempt was made by the same two ships. They were to splice the cable in mid-Atlantic this time and steam in opposite directions, but bad luck once more intervened. One of the worst storms ever recorded in Atlantic history bore down on the ships and during seven days the *Agamemnon* came near to sinking. The great mass of cable was hurled about and tangled, the coal bunkers broke and the coal was thrown about, resulting in many accidents to the crew. The ships ultimately met in mid-ocean and the cable was spliced at last. They had not gone many miles, however, before a breakage occurred and a fresh start was necessary. Twice again it happened and at last both ships had to give up the enterprise and return to Ireland for stores.

But in this era of electrical history courage was not lacking. Within a few weeks the ships were off again. This time both of them reached their destination without further accident and the Atlantic cable was completed. Wild rejoicing ensued and congratulatory messages were passed between the United States President and Queen Victoria, only to be followed by further disappointment. Within a few weeks the signals weakened and stopped. The cable was completely dead.

Economics plays an important role in the progress of science and engineering. Experiments have to be paid for, and so it was with the great submarine cable experiment. The failures had cost the stockholders about two and a half million dollars, but much had been learned, and in 1864 a new company was formed. The early setbacks continued in several more attempts, but at last in the year 1866 success was finally achieved and the first Atlantic cable was taken into commercial use. Today there are over twenty cables across the North Atlantic and among these are a few sections of some of the very early cables of a hundred years ago still giving useful service, lying at great depths in the ocean.

It was soon found that the needle telegraph instrument was not sufficiently sensitive to operate on the small currents traversing these long submarine cables and new methods were tried. The first of these was the famous "mirror speaking galvanometer" invented by Professor William Thomson (later Lord Kelvin), at the time the 1858 cable was laid. In this instrument the moving part of the galvanometer carried a tiny mirror onto which was thrown a beam of light which magnified the movements. The cable was capable of transmitting twenty-five words a minute in code, and special clerks capable of reading the flashing mirror at this speed were employed.

But this fast reading by eye caused many mistakes, so the next step was the invention of an instrument which made a permanent record. This was the famous "siphon recorder," again invented by Lord Kelvin, in which the incoming currents wrote a readable message, in code of course, on a strip of paper. The recorder could work much faster than an operator could read, so the tape could be transcribed by several writers without restricting the working of the cable. The siphon recorder proved invaluable and was used on cables all over the world until quite recent times when it has been superseded by further improvements.

The technical battle for increasing the speed and output of submarine cables has gone on continuously from the early days. The many improvements in method of operation, in the design of the cable, and in the terminal equipment employed form an important chapter in electrical development. An outstanding step forward was made by the introduction of duplex working. Instead of a message in only one direction at a time, as was done with the early cables, the duplex system enabled both ends to send and receive over the one single-wire cable at the same time.

Although at first sight this would appear to be an impossibility, the way of achieving the result is quite simple. The receiving circuit has a coil which is divided into halves, and the sending current at that station is injected into the middle of the coil. One half of the sending current goes out to the line and the other half goes through an artificial balancing line connected to the ground. In this way the outward currents balance one another in the receiving instrument and so do not interfere with the signals coming in.

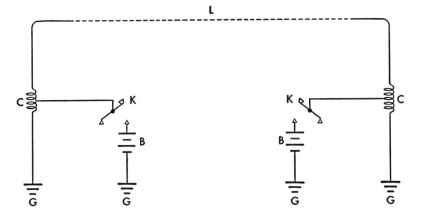

Principle of duplex working in early telegraph system. (B) Sending battery. (K) Sending key. (C) Coil of receiver. (G) Ground connection. (L) Line.

To increase the speed of operation in telegraph systems, automatic working is now widely employed. The fundamental principle today is the same as it had been for many years past. The message is first transferred in code to a punched paper tape which is then passed at high speed through a transmitter. This sends out currents to the line which operate a receiver and a printer, and this puts the message in plain language on a final strip. The first important automatic transmitter was invented by Wheatstone, and the Wheatstone high-speed system was employed universally for many years.

The punched tape is shown on the next page. A dot is represented by two holes side by side and a dash by two holes in a sloping direction. The arrangement of holes shown corresponds to the word *and*. When such a tape is passed rapidly through the Wheatstone transmitter, small metal pegs move into the holes and operate contacts at the appropriate intervals. At the receiving end another tape is printed with an ink line in Morse code, again as shown. The continuous row of dots down the center of the punched slip is provided for pulling the tape through the machine.

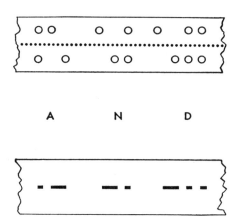

Punched tape for automatic telegraph transmission. The word "and" is shown at the bottom as Morse characters and above as it would appear on punched tape. Vertical holes mean a dot; sloping holes mean a dash.

A telegraphist operating the ordinary hand key cannot send more than about thirty words a minute, but the Wheatstone transmitter is capable of sending three hundred words a minute. In high-speed telegraphy the Morse code has now been superseded by the five-unit code. Instead of short and long signals, or dots and dashes, all signals are of the same duration. They are, however, in opposite directions, known as *marking* and *spacing* currents. By taking the five units in different combinations, we can more than cover the alphabet. We can take marking or spacing for the first position; that gives us two alternatives. Similarly we can use marking or spacing for the second position; that gives us four different combinations for the two positions, eight for three positions, sixteen for four positions, and thirty-two for five positions. We thus cover the twenty-six letters of the alphabet and have six combinations left over for other uses.

The tape is perforated automatically in a keyboard perforator, of which there are various types. The operation of perforation can be described as follows. Five metal combination bars lie side by side and have saw-tooth projections on their upper edge. Lying across the combination bars are a series of key bars, each one terminating in a key on what is virtually a typewriter keyboard. The depression of a key representing a certain letter moves the combination bars according to the code to give that same letter. The ends of the bars are connected through levers to five punches over which the paper is passed. When a key bar is depressed, it first of all moves the combination bars into the correct position and finally, when pressed down, operates a switch. This switch closes a circuit which connects current to a punching magnet and this presses upward those particular punches, one, two, three, four, or five, in any order as called for by the combination bars.

In sending the signal from the perforated tape, the automatic transmitter passes the tape quickly between a tape-retaining

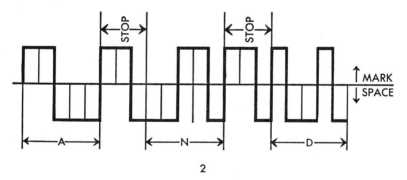

Five-unit telegraph code. (M) *Current in marking direction.* (S) *Current in reversed, or spacing, direction.* (1) *First three letters in alphabet.* (2) *The word "and" as received.*

plate and a striking guide plate. When a hole in the paper strip comes along, the metal striker moves forward and, through levers, closes an electric contact. Where there is no hole the metal striker remains stationary. The printing of telegrams has been known for a century, but during the past twenty or thirty years it has made tremendous strides. From forty words a minute the speed rose to sixty, then seventy-five, and today speeds of many hundreds of words a minute are obtainable with automatic switching.

The mechanism employed is very complicated but the general appearance of a modern machine is quite similar to a type-writer. It works on the standard five-unit code which is, of course, converted to ordinary letters and words on the usual page.

During recent years remarkable developments have taken place in long-distance submarine telephone cable. The first coaxial submarine cables made were three laid in 1921 between Key West, Florida, and Havana, Cuba, a distance of one hundred nautical miles. The insulation was gutta-percha; but, by using high-frequency carriers, each cable accommodated one telephone and three carrier telegraph circuits. In 1923 two further gutta-percha cables were installed off the Californian coast for carrier working.

In the rapidly developing field of submarine cables it is easy to recognize the progress, but a very good idea of what is being done can be found by tracing the change in design on a given route when cables are being added from time to time. Some good examples are to be found in Europe. Between 1922 and 1948 six submarine telephone cables were laid between England and Holland, a distance of eighty-two nautical miles. In 1950 one was laid from England to Denmark and two between Holland and Denmark.

The first cable was insulated with gutta-percha and there were four conductors at the four corners of a square. At intervals of one nautical mile loading coils were inserted to correct the distortion of the speech current.

The second cable, laid in 1924, was a revolutionary departure from the time-honored gutta-percha. The insulation was dry paper and, to keep out all moisture, a double lead sheath was applied. The conductors were arranged in four quads, that is, four groups each having four wires. The cable carried fourteen simultaneous conversations.

You will wonder how eight pairs of wires could produce fourteen circuits, but it can be done by what are called *phantom circuits*. In a quad of four wires, *A, B, C, D,* wires *A* and *C* carry one circuit, *B* and *D* a second and then, by connecting up coils at the end, a third circuit straddles *AC/BD*. Thus each quad provides three circuits on the four wires, which makes twelve circuits in the cable. Then if we call the quads *P, Q, R, S,* we can carry the superimposing procedure further by making a phantom circuit on *PR* and another on *QS*, so reaching our fourteen.

The next cable to be laid on this route in 1926 was not very different from the 1924 one—it had an extra wire down the center—but in 1937 a pair of cables of identical construction were laid. In these the coaxial principle was adopted and an improved gutta-percha used for the insulation. At this date, carrier working, which had been tried in numbers two and three, was adopted, providing seventeen circuits on the two double circuits, and "go" and "return" in each cable. Subsequently, without any modification to the cable itself, numbers four and five, the coaxial lengths, were made to carry thirty circuits.

The cable completed in 1948 is of the coaxial type but has an insulation partly of air and partly of *polyethylene,* which is now being used extensively in submarine cables. The central conductor is a single copper strand surrounded by ten copper wires and is covered with polyethylene. Over this is laid copper tapes to form a smooth cylinder. Polyethylene in the form of a rod is then wound on in an open spiral and more polyethylene as a solid tube follows. More tapes are applied before the jute yarn lappings and steel armoring wires. By the use of frequencies ranging from 24 to 804 kilocycles per second, this cable carries 84 simultaneous conversations.

In 1950 a coaxial cable was laid between England and Denmark, the longest coaxial submarine cable thus far constructed —over three hundred nautical miles. The construction was not very different from the earlier types but the insulation was a mixture of polyethylene and polyisobutylene and was solid. Initially, repeaters were connected at the two ends, which enabled fifteen simultaneous teleprinter circuits to work. Subsequently a repeater was inserted in the center of the cable and this made thirty-six teleprinter circuits available.

About the same time a pair of cables of the same construction was laid a distance of 142 nautical miles from Holland to Denmark. Each cable had two submerged repeaters and carried a total of thirty-six telephone channels.

For many years there has been a feeling that, although the submarine telegraph cables across the Atlantic and the telephone radio links between this country and Europe have provided a wonderful system of communication, the only satisfactory system would be a telephone cable. The telegraph cables enable personal messages, news, and stock prices to be transmitted; but these are one-way communications and are no substitute for the telephone in which two people can converse with one another as freely as if they were in the same room. Conversations became possible when radio services were established in 1907, but these are liable to interruption by atmospheric conditions. The need for a cable link was quite clearly felt, but it was evident that something quite different from the well-known telegraph cable was necessary.

There are many problems in transmitting speech over a long

cable. The current wave representing the speech becomes distorted and unintelligible. Further, the actual value of the current is attenuated so that only a small fraction of that which is put into the sending end reaches the receiving end. The problem increases as the frequency of the current increases. A reasonably satisfactory telegraph cable needs to transmit only about 150 impulses per second but, to transmit reasonable speech, at least 2500 cycles per second are necessary.

In the use of telephone cable on long-distance land circuits most of the problems involved have been solved, but on a land cable it is an easy matter to break in at intervals to insert items such as repeaters to boost the flagging current. In the case of faults during use the cable is accessible throughout its length. Moreover, because of the great cost of a submarine cable, it is necessary to get as many channels as possible so that a large number of people can speak at the same time and so provide a reasonable income for those providing the cable. All these points have been under consideration for some years and now the project has at last been achieved.

The length of the Atlantic crossing from Scotland to Newfoundland is two thousand nautical miles and in places the depth of water over the cable is two thousand fathoms. There are two separate cables and together they provide for thirty-six simultaneous conversations. Speech travels in one direction along one cable and in the opposite direction along the other cable.

In each length of cable there are fifty-two one-way repeaters, and each of these repeaters contains vacuum tubes and about sixty other electrical devices, such as resistors and transformers. Once the cable is laid it is a very difficult matter to replace any of the components which may become faulty. So all in all the Atlantic cable is a remarkable enterprise.

In our radio sets at home we can take out a tube and replace it. We can also connect the power supply for the filament and the plate with ease. But these tiny tubes tucked away inside the cable as much as a thousand miles from land and lying on the bed of the ocean at a depth of 2¼ miles have to be supplied with power from the ends of the cable. This is done through a single wire circuit and, as the plates and heaters require 55 volts on each repeater, a total of about 4000 volts is required for this purpose only.

The repeaters are each housed in cylindrical boxes held together end to end by spring connectors, and the armoring wires of the cable are carried right over the whole length of the repeater housing. Great care has been taken to keep out the least trace of sea water by the use of elaborate seals, and a further precaution has been taken of including a small dryer in with the apparatus at each point. As a milestone in electrical progress the completion of this transatlantic telephone cable is outstanding.

CHAPTER 11

The Free Electron

THE electron is too small to be seen and yet is known to flow in vast numbers through electric conductors to form a current. The electron is not always confined to a solid object like a copper wire, or even to a liquid as in a battery: it can move about in space. When we follow it beyond these confines, we enter the world of electronics where we meet the thermionic tube which made radio possible and led to the cathode ray tube, the basis of television. With their thousands of practical applications these two devices have contributed remarkably to the progress of science and to present-day life.

How is an electron freed from material objects? There is an atmosphere, or cloud, of electrons rushing about between the atoms of matter. In a conductor, these electrons drift along under the influence of any voltage applied in the circuit. No electrons leave the surface of the metal: the attraction of the positive charges keeps them under restraint.

If the temperature of the metallic conductor is raised, the rate of vibration of the atoms increases and the electrons between them begin to travel faster. At a certain critical temperature they approach the boundary at such a speed as to be freed, and they rush right out through the surface and away from the restraint of the mass of atoms trying to hold them in place. Because of

223

the different atomic structures of different substances, some part with their electrons at much lower temperatures than others and this fact is important in the design of radio tubes. If the filament of an incandescent electric bulb is used to generate free electrons, the temperature at which it becomes incandescent is just about sufficient to release the electrons. If, however, the filament is coated with certain oxides, such as barium, the electrons are released at a much lower temperature. In fact, a dull red heat is sufficient and this is the usual condition in radio tubes.

As the electrons in a thermionic tube move out of the hot element toward another plate in the tube, the emitting element is called the *cathode* and the second plate the *anode,* the terms used in chapter 3 in the discussion of electrolytic cells. The cathode may be heated in various ways. The simplest way is by the passage of an electric current, in which the current is passed directly through the wire joined in a convenient loop. Alternatively, the heating wire may be contained within a tubular cathode which it thus heats indirectly. Each type possesses advantages for certain particular uses.

When the electrons manage to escape, they present an interesting picture. After all the jostling and struggle within the metal they suddenly find themselves in a tranquil world with nothing pushing them about. The result is a crowd of electrons in the vicinity of the cathode, with the crowd thinning out toward the fringe where a few of the loiterers have strayed farther than most of the others.

To be really useful, an electron has to be pushed about, and one of the early discoveries made in this field was that the air or other gas in which the electrons were placed played an important role. It interfered with their movement and had to be removed. Removing gas from a space is the same as making a vacuum, and for that reason a thermionic tube is evacuated. By lowering the pressure of the gas we reduce the number of molecules of gas present, and there are fewer to interfere with the movement of the electrons. They can then move about with less risk of collision.

So far, then, in building up a picture of the thermionic tube we have arrived at this stage: when a metallic wire is heated, some of the contained electrons are helped to escape. By coating the wire with certain substances their escape is facilitated. When the electrons get out into space, they wait for something to happen, possibly being jostled a little by the remaining molecules of the gas. Removing the gas reduces this restraint and the electron is left the prey of any influence which may come along.

If the hot cathode is in a glass tube which has been evacuated, and a metallic anode is situated opposite the cathode, we have the very beginnings of the thermionic tube. In this form it is called the *diode*. Suppose you connect a low-tension battery giving, say, 2 volts so as to heat the cathode and, between the cathode and the anode, you connect a battery with a voltage of, say, 100. By means of a reversing switch and a milliammeter in the cir-

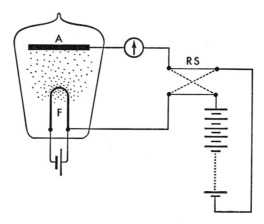

The diode as a rectifier. (F) Heated filament, or cathode. (A) Metal anode. (RS) Reversing switch. When A is made positive, current flows through the tube; when negative, no current flows.

cuit you can make this discovery: when the positive end of the battery is connected to the anode and the negative end to the cathode, a considerable current flows through the diode carried by the electrons.

When the battery is reversed and the positive end is connected to the cathode and the negative end to the anode, no current, or at any rate very little current, will flow through the diode. The reason is not far to seek; with the positive end to the anode the crowd of negative electrons is suddenly attracted to the positive anode and equally repelled from the negative cathode. If the current flows in the opposite position of the switch, the electrons are attracted by the positive cathode and repelled by the negative anode and so they stay where they are; even the stragglers suddenly retreat nearer the cathode. There is no current in this case, or possibly just a little current caused by a few wayward electrons. Thus the diode can conduct in one direction only and is a rectifier. This is the main purpose of the diode in radio work, to rectify an alternating current.

Valuable as it is, the contribution of the diode to electronics is small compared with that of the *triode* in which a third, or control, electrode is inserted between the cathode and the anode. The triode is essentially a device by which small electric powers can control large ones. The most general use is in amplifying a current or voltage as we have seen done in the repeaters of the transatlantic cable in the previous chapter. The triode also takes the unbelievably tiny currents received on radio sets and converts them into currents large enough to operate the loud-speaker. Other uses of the triode are in the generation of oscillations at very high frequency, up to thousands of millions a second, and in the modulation of signals for many purposes.

Why is it that such a simple device as the triode should have produced such revolutionary results? The third electrode, known as the *grid,* is a perforated plate or a coil of wire or any metallic

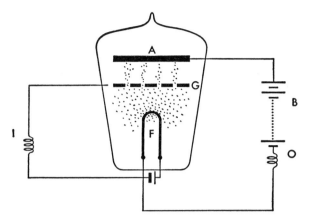

The triode. The input potential I *controls the passage of electrons through the grid* G *from the cathode* F *to anode* A. *Owing to the large battery* (B) *the input signal appears as a magnified output at* O.

form which has holes or spaces in it. As the grid is fixed between the cathode and the anode, its function is to control the flow of electrons from the former to the latter, and this control is effected by applying to the grid an electric potential. When the potential is negative—or, as we say, when the grid is given a negative bias —it repels the electrons approaching it on their way from the cathode to the anode. If the anode is positive at the time, then such grid bias keeping the electrons back reduces the anode current.

As there are spaces between the metal parts of the grid, a certain number of electrons escape the attempts of the grid to catch them, but by giving the grid sufficient bias the main anode current can be practically stopped. This is a powerful device by which a considerable amount of energy can be controlled by a small amount. A rough analogy would be the traffic on a busy avenue; when the lights turn from green to red, the automobiles stop, and when the lights change back again to green they all start off once more. In the triode we can do anything we like to the stream of electrons forming the current from the cathode to the anode simply by applying different voltages to the grid.

It follows at once that a triode is a valuable device for amplifying an alternating current. If a weak speech signal is received either from a radio aerial or over a long telephone circuit, we need only connect it to the grid of a triode and at once we can take from a high-voltage battery connected to the anode a faithful reproduction of the signal, but much more powerful. It is usual to employ a number of triodes together, one feeding into the next, to obtain many stages of amplification. By this means the output current may be many thousand times greater than the received or input current.

The triode, then, or thermionic tube, is a device for controlling one current by another (usually a weaker one). This device, employing the free electron or particular input current, results in a particular output current. Another remarkable device in which a current—or voltage, they are easily interchangeable —is applied is the *cathode-ray* tube.

In the cathode-ray tube, instead of holding back the electrons by means of electric potential on a grid, we collect them into a narrow pencil or beam as they fly from the cathode. Further, instead of collecting them on an anode to form a current outside the tube, we allow them to fall on a specially prepared surface on the end of the tube where they produce a bright spot which we can observe. By deflecting the beam of electrons about we can move the spot around on the screen and produce some most remarkable effects. (See the illustration on page 231.)

The shape of a cathode-ray tube is characteristic. It is roughly a glass cone a foot or less in length, with a tubular extension at the small end and a flat, slightly curved sheet at the large end. The electron beam travels from the small end to the viewing screen on the large end, which may be anything from a few inches to a foot or more in diameter.

The tube is, of course, evacuated or contains a very small quantity of special gas, and the electrons are generated at a cathode which may be a heated filament or a metal tube surrounding the heating filament. A short distance in front of the cathode is a plate or tube with a central hole. This electron gate, which is maintained at a high positive potential, attracts the electrons. Those that pass through the hole form a fast-moving stream which flies the length of the tube and strikes the fluorescent viewing screen, forming a luminous spot. By adjusting the potential on the plate, we can dim or brighten the image on the screen at will.

Because it is necessary to have a hole large enough to allow a sufficient number of electrons to pass, it will be obvious that the spot on the screen has an appreciable size. Since it causes blurring, this is undesirable. To secure a small intense spot, a focusing device is introduced. This cannot be a glass lens as in a camera, but very simple arrangements are found to be quite effective. If two anodes are used, one in front of the other, and the second one is held at a higher voltage than the first, the electrons passing from one to the other are found to crowd together. Sometimes, you will notice, when water passes out from a hole in a plate, the sides of the jet curve inward. The same sort of crowding of electrons takes place as they pass from the low-voltage anode to the high-voltage anode. The emerging beam is small and intense and produces a tiny bright spot on the viewing screen. With such an electron lens the focusing is just a matter of adjusting the voltage on the controlling anode.

Having now produced a bright spot on the screen, we must look into the arrangements adopted for moving the spot about in order to produce a display in the form of lines of light, or traces. These build up the pictures in television. One of several methods, and one which is in wide use, is to provide two pairs of metal plates in the tube, one pair at right angles to the other, in such a position that the electron beam passes first through the space between one pair and then through the space between the second pair as indicated in the diagram.

When a voltage is applied between two plates through which an electron is passing, the electron is attracted toward the positive plate, and the beam is deflected. If the plates are horizontal and the upper plate is made positive, the beam will be deflected upward and the position of the spot in the viewing screen will rise. Conversely, if the lower plate is made positive, the beam will be deflected downward and the spot will move down from its central position. The extent of the movement of the spot is determined by the magnitude of the voltage applied to the plates. If a positive potential of 100 volts on the upper plate raised the spot one inch, then 200 volts would raise it two inches. When the electron beam passes between a second pair of plates, in this case disposed vertically, and a voltage is applied between the plates, the spot is moved horizontally to the left with positive potential on one plate and to the right with positive potential on the other plate. Again the extent of the deflection is controlled by the magnitude of the applied voltage. By suitable adjustment of voltage on the two pairs of plates, the spot can be made to move to any part of the screen.

The great value of the cathode-ray tube is in the display of rapidly changing effects usually associated with alternating currents. It is necessary to have two movements of the spot at right angles to one another. Suppose we apply an alternating voltage from the power line to the horizontal plates, the X plates. The spot will move up and down and will draw a straight vertical line on the screen. Owing to the phenomenon known as *persistence of vision*—the tendency to see an image for a fraction of a second after the object has disappeared—we see a line and not a series of spots in different positions. The retina of our eye holds the individual impressions so that all run together and produce the solid line. But this does not tell us much about what is going

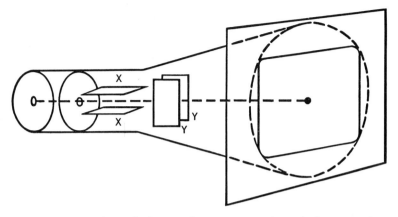

Main features of a cathode-ray tube. Two pairs of metal plates at right angles cause the beam to move horizontally and vertically, so covering the whole screen. Application of a varying voltage between the two X plates moves the beam up and down, between the Y plates horizontally.

on while the spot is moving up and down. Is it going the same speed all the time or is it going in jumps; if so, how does it jump?

A very simple refinement called the *time base* establishes the great value of the cathode-ray tube. While the spot is racing up and down, it is moved horizontally by means of the vertical Y plates so it can be watched more carefully. A source of voltage for the Y plates could be obtained by connecting a high resistance across the terminals of a battery and, through a sliding contact, picking up the voltage from zero to full voltage.

By arranging the resistance, or potentiometer as it really is, in the form of a circle and driving it by means of a motor we can apply to the Y plates every so often a voltage starting from zero and gradually building up to the full voltage of the battery, then dropping again suddenly to zero. If, without any voltage on the X plates, we apply such an arrangement to the Y plates, the spot will move steadily across the screen and then suddenly jump back and start again. Suppose we adjusted our potentiometer motor to repeat this operation sixty times a second, then the spot would move across the screen in the horizontal base line in a sixtieth of a second, fly back in an infinitely short time, then across again, and in a sixtieth of a second fly back again and so on. We have thus established a time base.

While the spot is flashing backward and forward under the operation of our potentiometer time base, let us connect the 60-cycle power-line voltage to the X plates. What we shall see immediately is the sine curve. While the line's alternating voltage is causing the spot to move up and down vertically, our time base has spread it out horizontally. The value of the cathode-ray tube is established. In this form the cathode-ray tube is known as an oscilloscope.

Engineers who are bothered about peculiar effects on an electric system can connect up an oscilloscope and see at once whether there is any explanation in the shape of the voltage curve. In a thousand ways it provides a new eye whereby we can see effects which occur much too rapidly to see in the ordinary way.

The most important application of the cathode-ray tube is in television. Two fundamental modifications are introduced, however. For convenience in use, the tube is shortened by making the screen end steeper. And, instead of the beam's being deflected by electrostatic charges on two pairs of plates, it is deflected by the electromagnetic field in two pairs of coils. From what has been said in earlier chapters it will be clear that in the electrostatic system the electrons in the beam move in a direction from one plate of a pair to the other, while in the electromagnetic system they move at right angles to the magnetic field created by the coils. The resulting movement of the spot on the screen is the same under either system.

The problem of seeing at a distance by means of electrical transmission has been discussed for many years. When it was discovered in 1875 that the electrical resistance of the metal

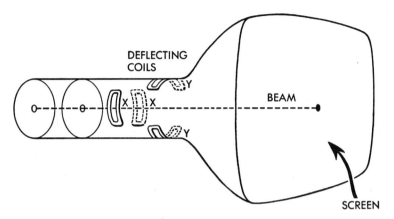

Operation of a television tube. The X pair of coils moves the beam vertically; the Y pair moves it horizontally.

selenium was changed when light falls on it, the idea of using the effect for picture transmission occurred to many people. One scientist proposed to make a mosaic of tiny selenium cells which would imitate the human eye, and many other scientists in the following years attempted to carry out this and similar ideas. An important step forward was made when, instead of trying to transmit the whole picture at once, the idea of *scanning* was developed. In scanning, the picture is divided into a large number of small elements and a signal is taken from each in turn.

A scientist named Baird produced a mechanical scanner in the form of a rapidly revolving disk with holes which distributed the light from different elements in the picture to a series of photoelectric cells. The current from these cells was made to affect the light from a neon tube at the receiving station and this passed through a similar disk onto a screen. Recognizable images were produced by this method.

To make a satisfactory picture clear and free from flicker it must be divided up into a very large number of elements, and a present-day television picture contains over 200,000 such elements. As we depend on persistence of vision, all these separate elements need to be reproduced again and again rapidly in succession to make the picture appear continuous. In the ordinary motion picture the screen is illuminated intermittently 24 times a second and between one picture and the next there is a period of darkness. Owing to persistence of vision, our eyes retain the picture for the period during which no light comes from the screen and subsequent pictures become connected as one picture in our mind. When an object is slightly displaced picture after picture, we get the sensation of movement in the object. The same principle applies in television. The 200,000 elements are scanned in a small fraction of a second and scanned again and again, 30 times a second.

To transmit the signals from 200,000 elements of a picture 30 times a second calls for the transmission of 6 million signals every second. The mechanical device experimented with by Baird was soon found to be quite incapable of meeting the requirements. The nimblest thing in the universe had been discovered in the electron by Professor J. J. Thomson at Cambridge, England, and in 1908 a flood of light was thrown on the problem of producing successful television by another Englishman, Campbell Swinton. In a letter to *Nature,* on June 4, 1908, he wrote as follows:

> This part of the problem can probably be solved by the employment of two beams of cathode rays (one at the transmitting and one at the receiving station) synchronously deflected by the varying fields of two electromagnets placed at right angles to each other so that the extremities of the two beams are caused to sweep synchronously over the whole of the required surfaces within the one-tenth of a second necessary to take advantage of visual persistence. The real difficulty lies in devising an efficient transmitter which, under the influence of light and shade, shall sufficiently vary the transmitted electric current so as to produce the necessary alterations in the

intensity of the cathode beam of the receiver. Possibly no photo-electric phenomenon at present known will provide what is required in this respect, but should something suitable be discovered distant electric vision will, I think, come within the region of possibility.

Here we see the very fundamental basis of modern television predicted in an astonishing manner at a time when radio tubes were almost unknown, but it was a quarter of a century before Campbell Swinton's prediction took practical form. The problem was to convert the variation in the light which constitutes a picture to a varying electric current with some 6 million signals a second. Success was achieved by Vladimir Zworykin, an American, in 1933 with a device which he named the *iconoscope*.

The operation of the iconoscope depends on photoelectric effects. When light falls on a metal surface, electrons are emitted from the metal. The number of electrons emitted depends on the intensity of the light and on the nature of the surface. The effect, known as the surface photoelectric effect, is very small but is sufficient to be measured and is used as the basis for a television camera.

In Zworykin's iconoscope a mosaic of tiny particles is produced by depositing silver globules on a thin sheet of mica about 4 inches square. These particles, too small to be distinguished by the naked eye, are insulated from one another and the mica sheet is backed by a metal plate. It will be seen that each particle forms a microscopic electric condenser with the mica insulating it from the metal plate behind.

The mosaic is set up in a glass bulb from which the air has been evacuated, and by means of a lens very similar to that used in an ordinary photographic camera the scene to be transmitted is focused onto it as shown on page 236. In an extension tube set at an angle is situated an electron gun with its heated cathode, control grid, and anode very similar to the details of the cathode-

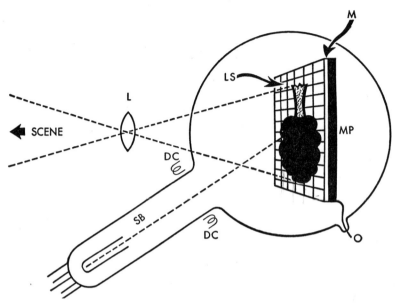

The construction of the iconoscope; the basis of the television camera.
(SB) Beam of electrons scanning LS. *(LS) Mosaic of light-sensitive*
material. (MP) Metal backing plate. (M) Sheet of thin mica. (DC) De-
flecting coil. (L) Lens. (O) Outlet wire.

ray tube already described. By means of the electron gun a stream
of electrons is projected onto the mosaic; and, by means of
electromagnetic coils near the neck of the tube, the beam is
made to scan the mosaic from side to side in lines repeated
vertically one after the other.

The operation of the iconoscope television camera is as follows: At any particular instant the illuminated mosaic is giving up electrons by the photoelectric effect, the brightly illuminated elements giving up many electrons and the less brightly
illuminated only a few. The thousands of elements all assume
different electric potentials relative to the plate behind them. At
a prearranged signal the scanning beam then sweeps over the
surface and all elements are recharged to the same potential by
the electrons shot at them. By means of a metallic collecting ring

the small charges emitted from the elements due to the light are collected between the ring and the back plate and passed on to amplifying tubes. In this way the scanning of the complete mosaic produces a rapidly changing current which represents the scene focused on the mosaic.

In the iconoscope a picture is converted into a varying electric current just as a sound is converted into an electric current with the microphone in telephony. In television the current from the iconoscope is called the *video* signal and the whole picture is transmitted 30 times every second. There are about 200,000 elements of current transmitted for each time the picture is scanned and the current varies 6 million times a second. We talk of the television transmission channel being 6 megacycles wide. Different stations use different frequencies so as not to interfere with one another but each has a band of 6 megacycles. For instance, one station may operate at frequencies between 60 and 66 megacycles and another at either 54 and 60 or 66 and 72 without any interference with each other.

The original iconoscope has been greatly improved and other types of cameras have been converted. The main alternative, the *image orthicon,* catches the reflected electrons in the beam.

As the electron beam in the transmitter iconoscope scans the mosaic in the pickup tube, it travels from the bottom upward, line by line. At the receiver it travels from the top downward. This is because we want to see the picture the right side up while on the iconoscope it is upside down because of the viewing lens.

Complete synchronization between the two beams in the television circuit is necessary. The beam at the receiver must move exactly with that at the transmitter, otherwise the picture would be completely fuzzy. If the spot on the receiver is moving across the nose of the lady we are looking at and the spot at the transmitter is on her eye we cannot expect a very good likeness. To maintain synchronization a device called a *sync* generator, or *sync,* is employed. The sync signal tells the receiver tube when to begin the trace.

In the 525-line television system, which is standard in the United States, the spot moves across the screen, starting on the top line and moving down, line by line. After it has reached the end of the line it jumps back to the beginning of the next line to be scanned and traverses that one. This is done by means of a current with a sawtooth wave. Instead of the famous and usual sine wave, the current in the sawtooth wave slowly grows to a maximum and then, toward the end of the cycle, drops suddenly. To provide for scanning 525 lines 30 times a second, the current controlling this feature has a frequency of 30×525, or 15,750 a second. But that is not all. The sync system has not only to move the spots across the picture correctly, it also has to move them down the picture, line by line, and when they reach the bottom, jump them up to the top again ready for the next go. Again a sawtooth current is used for this purpose but, as this movement is much less frequent, the current frequency is much lower. Since there are 30 complete pictures, or frames, a second you would guess that this frequency would be 30; but that is not quite correct for another reason:

To prevent interference with the picture while the spot is returning from the bottom to the top, a blackout period is interposed, but if there are 30 blackout periods per second—that is, as many as the number of frames per second—a certain amount of flicker is noticed. This is avoided by a system called *interlacing.* When the lines are scanned they are not done in the order 1, 2, 3, 4, etc., going down the picture; but alternate ones are missed. The spot, after tracing line 1, jumps to line 3 and then to line 5. On reaching the bottom of the picture it then jumps up to line 2 and completes the even numbers omitted in the first round. Thus, you will see, the vertical sweep has to be done twice for every frame and the frequency is not 30 but 60.

In this way the number of blackouts is 60 every second and, owing to the persistence of vision in the person viewing the picture, there is no flicker.

A simple sweep across the tube takes under fifty-millionths of a second and all the sweeps from top to bottom are completed in under sixteen-thousandths of a second. These are the slow movements. The quick jump of the spot after completing one line trace to the beginning of the next trace occupies less than ten-millionths of a second!

What has been said about television applies principally to monochromatic, or black-and-white, television. There are no insuperable difficulties in introducing color. It is only a question of viewing the scene at the transmitting end through screens having the three primary colors and providing similar screens at the receiving tube. The three colors have to be scanned in sequence and, if they succeed each other at a sufficient rate, the colors blend quite naturally in the received picture. The color screens at the sending and receiving end must be synchronized with one another, and the transmission of all this additional information in the video signal means speeding up the scanning rate in the camera and receiver tube and requires still further increases in the frequencies of the transmission waves.

241